Facing It

The Interactive Handbook of
DOs, DON'Ts and DAREs
for Handicapped People
and their Caregivers

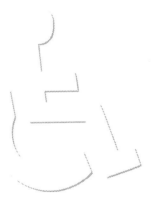

Pam Van Hook

J+P
ink

J and P Ink — an imprint of
Pam Van Hook Ministry Beaverton, Oregon

FACING IT: The Interactive Handbook of DOs, DON'Ts and DAREs for Handicapped People and their Caregivers.

Copyright © 2005 by Pam Van Hook.

Published by J & P Ink

> an imprint of Pam Van Hook Ministry
> 4130 SW 117th Ave #296
> Beaverton, OR 97005.

Bible quotations, unless otherwise noted, are from the *HOLY BIBLE: NEW INTERNATIONAL VERSION* © (NIV®). Copyright © 1973, 1978, 1984 by International Bible Society. Used by permission of Zondervan Publishing House.

First printing, 2008

Printed in the United States of America.

ISBN 978-0-9801012-3-2

The purpose of this book is to help handicappers and caregivers experience, through an interactive series of DOs, DON'Ts and DAREs, what it takes to FACE physical disability, well.

This book is dedicated to each and every one of you,
handicappers and caregivers,
from the heart of one who cares.

Contents

Preface — Pre-FACING IT

Here is little bit of Pre-FACING IT information to help you understand how to use this book and where I stand on politically correct terminologies.

First of all, FACING IT is intended to be a hands-on experience for the reader. All through this book the reader is invited to personally interact with me through an integrated series of DOs, DON'Ts and DAREs. Appropriate icons accompany each DO, DON'T and DARE so each is easy to identify and remember.

Second, since I call this book an interactive handbook of DOs, DON'Ts and DAREs for Handicappers and Caregivers, I'd better explain why I prefer the term "Handicapped" to the now more politically correct term, "Disabled." I think I am amply qualified to speak my opinion here. (Take a quick look at the back of the book.) "Handicapped" has two dictionary definitions and "Disabled" has only one. The two definitions of "Handicapped" are "(1) having a condition that markedly restricts one's ability to function physically, mentally or socially, and (2) a disadvantage imposed on a superior competitor in order to make the chances more equal." Even though I am the first definition, I dearly love the second definition." In it, "Handicapped" implies physical prowess, strength, or any exceptional ability that needs to be held back so others have a chance to equally compete. Think of racing, golf, sailing, hopscotch, tiddlywinks, etc. The need to be "Handicapped" in any competition means the competitor possesses superior ability.

To me, the term "Handicapped" speaks of strength and action placed at a disadvantage. I can handle that and even feel empowered in the midst of my many handicaps. The term "Disabled" has just one definition and frankly, it sticks in my craw. I know. I know. It's just me, but here's why. To me, "Disabled" brings to mind a broken down vehicle that has to be pushed to the side of the road until a tow truck comes to haul it away to the junkyard. The dictionary describes "Disabled" as "a person having a physical or mental condition that limits their movements, senses, or activities." I am "Disabled" but I way prefer to live my life as a "Handicapper," a person of strength and action that has been placed at a disadvantage. I use both terms in this book, but now you know my preference when it comes to politically correct terminology.

Okay, Handicappers and Caregivers, on to the Introduction.

INTRODUCTION:
DO YOU HAVE TO FACE IT?

Chances are if you're looking at these words you are the one having to FACE IT, or possibly you are the one who cares for someone who is having to FACE IT. This book is for you, from me — one who has had to FACE IT and continues daily to FACE IT.

"IT," defined in this book, is a physical disability or handicap that forcibly invades a so-called "normal lifestyle." This "IT" can mean no more normal walking, eating, breathing, seeing, hearing, working, playing, writing, driving, speaking, exercising, hunting, camping, sewing, fishing, gardening, cooking, and on and on and on … you name "IT."

Any physical handicap can be personally devastating. I know. But I have good news. You now hold in your hands a plan and a method to FACE any of life's challenges with meaningful and purposeful action. Meaning and purposeful action makes life worth living. Having a plan and a method in hand is a good thing.

Since the summer of 1999, I've gained valuable personal experience in how to FACE IT and I'm ready to share these DOs, DON'Ts and DAREs with you. I am not a health care professional, therapist, nurse or doctor. I don't want to be. I am, however, an experienced Handicap Permit holder. My only qualification to even begin a discussion of DOs, DON'Ts and DAREs is that I am definitely a handicapped person who is FACING IT every day.

In this book, we will look at some natural human reactions to the in-your-face bad news of physical handicaps. We will call these THE 5 Fs and the BIG D: FAILURE • FRUSTRATION • FURY • FEAR • FINALITY and DEPRESSION. Together, we'll consider and write about these 5 Fs of Reaction to Physical Disability, Depression, and how we can best adapt. Together, we'll think and write concerning DOs, DON'Ts and DAREs for each of these 5 Fs and the Big D.

Then, together, we'll look at some good CHOICES we can make to FACE well the hard news that may be with us for the rest of our lives. We'll call these good CHOICES THE 4 Fs: FAITH • FAMILY • FRIENDS • A

FUTURE FACE TO FACE MEETING. It is so good to know that no matter what our handicap is, we, as handicappers and caregivers, have help, hope and CHOICES. Together, we'll read and write our way through these 4 good Fs as well.

Come on now. Let's go. I guarantee a wild ride. You and I together. Just don't forget your handicap permit. Let's FACE IT.

WHO AM I?

Who am I to write about such things? Good question. Since this is an interactive handbook of DOs, DON'Ts and DAREs for handicappers and caregivers, I'll try to keep this short and sweet, so we can get to the stuff that matters.

I am a daughter, a sister, a wife, a mama, a grandma, a mother-in-law, daughter-in-law, sister-in-law, an auntie, and a follower of Jesus of Nazareth. I'm also quite physically handicapped.

For the last 5 years I've been a certified, permit-carrying handicapper. Oh, the joy. The reason this book even came to mind was that I was not FACING IT very well. I had every support system in the world in place and I was still down and out and facing the BIG D (Depression) way too many days and nights. I was loved and cared for in precious and priceless ways by my husband, my family, my friends, my church and my God. What was wrong?

One very desperate, dark and lonely morning this pre-menopausal, empty nester, handicapper grandma had had it. It was only 10 a.m. and I had done everything I could physically manage to do around the house. Well, truthfully, all I wanted to do. My husband was at work. I had completed all my Bible study work (they let me lead and teach at our church) and then some. Now it was just the old dog and me in an empty house that I couldn't escape without calling out for help. My total loss of independence and impaired mobility came crashing down around me. I knew I was in real trouble, even with all the help I could ever want just a phone call or a prayer away. I chose prayer. And got an answer. Immediately. "Write a book." I saw the cover of the book — the blue and white handicapped permit that constantly hangs in the face of every disabled person as they drive or are driven around. And I saw the title of the book — FACING IT. What an idea! What a title! Have you seen my face!? (Look at the back cover.) Who says God doesn't have a sense of humor?

Me, write a book? I'm not a writer. I'm a talker. On all the personality and leadership tests I've ever taken I show up as an Otter/Lion, ranking quite low in the Beaver/Golden Retriever modes. This means I love to facilitate discussion, lead in any way possible, direct things in a big way, work from outlines and speak the large picture with gusto! Not sit at a computer with only one functional eye and dwell on the details word by word. But on that dark and desperate morning, as I prayed, I was given a commission to write this book, for my benefit as well as for yours.

Since I know I'm really a talker, not a writer, it may seem to you, the reader, as if I'm talking this thing to you. I am. Please humor me, and if I ask you a question, just jump in and answer me back as if we are talking together. Will you do that? Often, I'm also going to ask you to write in response to questions I ask. I hope you like to write more than I do.

As I sit here beginning this process, I can see how God has prepared me for this adventure in life as a handicapper, and now as a writer. In the 1960s my baby brother used to love to torment me with the worst word he could think of at the time — Spaz! Well, some 40 years later, I've lived into that title he so loved to throw at me. In the summer of 1999 something went terribly wrong with this body I live in. The best guess a vast array of doctors could come up with, was that a virus hit my system and my body punched back like Sylvester Stallone in Rocky on fast-forward. My own auto-immune system damaged my spinal cord, the main nerve to my right eye, and took out my pancreas, leaving me with Type I diabetes and 4 shots of insulin a day. I was 51 years old. The doctors can only observe the damage. The biggest neurological problem I continue to FACE is spastic inflexibility of my legs. I am a Spaz! I now wear the title reluctantly, but fairly well, having lived with it for many of my childhood years. God was preparing me.

In spite of this name calling as a child, I dearly loved my brother and was dearly loved not only by him, but also by my mom and dad and extended family. I was the only girl on my father's side of the family and I truly was a Princess in their eyes, as well as my own. It just didn't matter that I was skinny, bucktoothed and had worn glasses since the first grade. They thought I was beautiful and so did I. So now, as I look out into the world and into the mirror with one dark black lens and one clear lens (*Arrrr, matey*) and dependently lean on my bright red walker, I can truthfully acknowledge that, after a period of adjustment, I am comfortable with and even enjoy my unique outward appearance.

One other key part of my makeup is that I love to lead and direct other people. I can clearly remember telling my childhood circle of friends that if they wanted to play with me, they had to do what I wanted them to do. And they did. So even though I know my strengths are speaking and leading others, in the writing of this book, I still get to lead and direct you, the reader, word by word. Cool. God is very good.

Beyond my basic personality and God-given talents, my Lord was at work preparing me for this task at hand years before my life changing physical disabilities. At age 13 I knew the certain call of God on my life and realized my need to respond. I accepted the One and only Son of God, Jesus Christ, as my very own Savior, and wonder of wonders, the Holy Spirit of the Living God entered my life! The problem however, was that it took me 30 more years to allow Him to be my Lord. At age 13, in our little Baptist church, I thought Savior was enough.

On Palm Sunday at Beaverton Christian Church I was 30 years away from age 13 and my acceptance of Jesus as my Savior. It was a beautiful spring morning. As I listened to our pastor painfully and tenderly explain what Jesus endured on the cross for me, I began to realize my prideful and arrogant ways. I was not my own. I belonged to Another. I was deeply moved. At the end of his sermon, he said, "This is what Jesus has done for you. What are you doing for Him?" What? What? Something was required of me beyond accepting Him as Savior? Yes. Yes, indeed, and that very morning of my 43rd year on earth I began to pursue Him and allow Him to pursue me as Lord of all I am or ever hope to be. And He has been faithful even when I haven't been. I immediately joined a Bible study class and began to finally live into what God, not Princess Pam, wanted in my life.

Ours is a large church with many opportunities to study the Bible and experience the reality of the risen Lord. We have many gifted teachers and I was eager to learn about God and what was in the Bible. I was finally ready to begin to know my Savior and Lord and experience the reality of His life in my life. Amazing! I was mentored and nurtured in this growth process and within a couple years it was my immense privilege to be asked to lead a women's' Bible study. A perfect fit! It has been my joy and honor to continue in this role for the last 12 years. This Princess has been allowed to speak before groups of women and even to our entire congregation some Sundays, making use of a B.A. in Speech earned during my college years. Boy, do I love a microphone! The microphone for this assignment from my Lord is now this computer keyboard. Trust me. I'd much rather be speaking this to you from an outline with a microphone in hand, than punching out every word here alone at this desk. But, if I've learned anything since that wonderful Palm Sunday, it is to listen to my Lord and obey, immediately.

Ok. Enough about me, let's get on with the important nuts and bolts of this so-called interactive handbook of DOs, DON'Ts and DAREs for handicappers and those who care for us.

It's time to begin interacting. In the box below, write down the "IT" you are FACING as a handicapper or a caregiver. There may be multiple "ITS." As an example, my "ITS" are: Type 1 diabetes, one functioning eye, and unexplained neurological issues that cause discomfort, pain, visual and spatial disorientation, and spastic inflexibility in my legs. More importantly, I have to face *these* "ITS" every day: 4 insulin shots, a strict dietary regime, and significantly impaired movement requiring a walker and keeping me from driving, jumping, running, and a whole host of normal activities. All marked by the inevitable hanging of the blue handicap parking permit.

Don't be shy about this. Be honest. This may be very difficult to do. It was for me. Please know you are not alone and that help and hope are in this handbook. This is your first opportunity to begin the process of FACING IT. What is your "IT?"

Part I

The 5 Fs of Reaction to Disability:
FAILURE · FRUSTRATION · FURY · FEAR · FINALITY

REACTION – Definition: a feeling experienced in response to a situation or an event.

The 5 Fs we are going to interact with in this section of our handbook are five basic, normal, natural, human reactions to the invasion of a debilitating physical handicap. Whether this handicap is gradual or sudden, minimal or major, I have found these 5 Fs of Reaction to Disability to be present. Not necessarily in the order I've arranged — please feel free to choose your own arrangement. But be warned. All five of these nasty Fs *will* try to push you around, sometimes one at a time, and sometimes all five at once.

I neglected to share one thing with you in the WHO AM I? Section. It is this: I HATE ROLLER COASTERS. And guess what? Living with these 5 Fs is like living on The Colossus at Six Flags Magic Mountain. Gulp. These 5 Fs are never static. They are either heading up or down, or whipping us around a curve, or smashing us into the one sitting closest to us. Double gulp. Maybe you love the thrill of a roller coaster. OK. I know a few crazy people who do. But we're talking 24 hours a day, 365 days a year on that slippery track, with no level ground. Triple gulp. If you're ready for the ride of your life, let's slide into our cramped little car and brace for a wild ride. …

DO – Readers

DO realize that all 5 of these Fs are OK and probably necessary to experience for both the handicapper and the caregiver: FAILURE • FRUSTRATION • FURY • FEAR • FINALITY. (In this interactive handbook we are FACING physical disabilities. But please DO realize we are all complex individuals. Each of us has a physical, emotional, mental, and spiritual life. When we are challenged in any of these areas, all areas of our lives will be affected in some way. DO be aware as we proceed.)

 ## DON'T – Readers

DON'T camp out in any of the 5 Fs for too long or the BIG D will hit with a vengeance. That BIG D is DEPRESSION. I speak from experience. (Figuring out how to follow this DON'T is the subject of the rest of this book.)

 ## DARE – Readers

Let's be bold and take the DARE ride! Let's DARE to explore the ups, downs, dips, twirls and curves for each of the 5 Fs of Reaction to Physical Disability. Just please sit close to me and allow me to scream my brains out as we take on the track together.

As we climb into the car to begin this ride, I want to make sure we're all belted in, arms and legs are safely inside, and the ride will be as smooth as it can be. In addition to all the DOs, DON'Ts and DARES for each of the 5 Fs of Reaction to Physical Disability, there's one essential action we need to take for all the reactions. Here it is.

DO – Handicappers

DO begin to keep a daily log or journal. I'll give you tips about what to journal for each individual F of Reaction, but right now start a journal if you haven't already done so. Be consistent in this journaling and it will assist you in adapting to new expectations of your own physical functioning. Try to throw some humor into it at least once a day.

If the idea of daily journaling is new to you, don't freak out or give up on the idea. Daily journaling will help you FACE your "IT" — and I'll help you learn how to do it simply, quickly, and creatively. This is an experience you don't want to miss. Just trust me.

If you are already one who journals, this will be a new way to experience the benefits of daily journaling as you FACE disability. So no matter where you are at this moment, help is on the way. Following the upcoming DARE, I will show you what I mean by daily *FACING IT* journaling.

> *Before using the* Facing It Journal, *I kept a very minimal personal journal detailing daily events in my life. I would write phrases instead of sentences, initials instead of names, draw pictures, and scribble shorthand notes to myself. You get the picture, right? I told you already, I'm no writer. But this journal of sorts proved invaluable in terms of tracking my life, physically, mentally, emotionally and spiritually along with the lives of those I love. So, for about nine years before the* Facing It Journal *became available, I had a taste of the value of daily journaling. And it was good.*

Handicapper, have you ever kept a daily journal? Do you like to write? Or do abbreviations, phrases, and stick figures fit you like they fit me? No matter your writing skills, can you see the value of a daily journal? This is one of those places you can answer me right back, out loud or on paper. I recommend paper, because the very first interactive DO in this book is a recommendation to begin writing down your daily experiences. How do you feel about keeping a written record of your experiences and Reactions to Physical Disability? (Probably about as good as I felt about it.) But from experience, I can assure you this is one good DO to DO. Please write your reactions to this DO now.

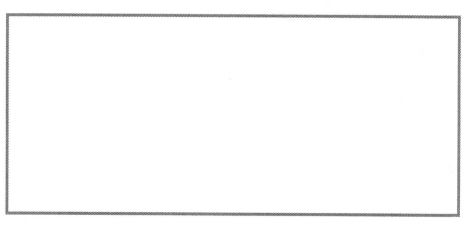

 DO – Caregivers

You too, Caregivers, please DO begin a journal, from your point of view. Please note that the instructions above for the handicappers apply to you caregivers as well. Each of these journals will be very personal so sharing is optional. Hopefully, at some point in the process of FACING IT together, both handicapper and caregiver will be able to compare notes in love and acceptance. How do you feel about keeping a daily journal? Do you like to write? Can you see the value to yourself and your capper of recording daily events, emotions, etc? You know I'm going to recommend you DO this. It will be well worth your efforts. Please write your response to these questions.

 DON'T – Handicappers

DON'T ignore this essential DO! Please consider journaling. I'll help you. Keep reading.

 DON'T – Caregivers

DON'T ignore the first DO! Please consider journaling. I'll help you. Keep reading.

In the middle of writing this book, something happened that reminded me of the importance of daily journaling. It's a longish story, with dark humor, tenderness, rage, and a humbling of the Princess writer. I can't think of a better way to tell you how important keeping a journal is. I'll usually put my personal stories in a box like you do, but I'm going to treat this story like a newspaper article (see next page.)

The Rotten Onion Episode —
A True Confession

It was Friday evening and I had no idea what stinky darkness was lurking in the heart and mind of this supposed super-handicapper, turned author. I hadn't kept track of my reactions, choices and attitudes in my *Facing It Journal* for at least two weeks, so no wonder.

After almost six years into my physical disabilities you'd think I would have a better grip on my reactions. Nope. The moment my closest caregiver (husband Jim) suggested we go food shopping on a Friday evening, I began to lean into the fan that soon, very soon, I would hit.

When I was physically normal I used to make it a point to make early Tuesday morning runs to the store, so I could choose the freshest produce and enjoy the luxury of wheeling a cart up and down spacious, un-crowded aisles. However, as a dependent handicapper, I now had to be hauled around by someone else and shop when it was convenient for them, assisted by them. This translated into zero shopping independence. I hated this. I still hate this. It is a constant reminder that I am handicapped and need help to accomplish ordinary, simple tasks.

So, that Friday evening, as Jim drove us to the store, my attitude was already dark with resentment as I pictured the crowds jamming the aisles and the crummy leftover, pawed-over, remaining produce that awaited our arrival. He was his usual self, happy to be with me. Happy to get his housebound wife out of the house, and looking forward to spending time shopping together with his sweetheart of almost thirty years. Meanwhile, I was busy turning into the wicked witch of the northwest.

By the time we parked in the incredibly far-away-from-the-front-door handicapped parking space, I had completely transformed from the more commonly known perky, upbeat smiling Pam, into sarcastic, belligerent, bent on confrontation, scowling Pam. Friday night shoppers beware!

I was right. I told Jim so. The place was jammed with carts and weekend shoppers. It was trashed, shopped out and the floors were dirty. One look with my one good eye made me grimace as I anticipated joining the teeming masses. Of course the cart I chose to hang onto for balance and stability was a squeaker and a right hand leaner. It was my destiny that night, and I refused to give it up because I was somehow "enjoying" the torture of it all. I was mad. Mad at my body's stupid failures; mad at my inability to control my attitude; and mad at the shopping cart. I was inadvertently ramming the corners of the produce aisles and coming dangerously close to hitting other shoppers. I got madder. During all this Jim stayed amazingly calm and sweet. He tried valiantly to channel my frustration and fury into positive actions with humor and help. He can almost always get me to laugh at myself or a situation, but not this night. No way. So he did the smart thing. He suggested we part ways and he would do the bulk of the shopping. All he asked me to do was make my cart-lurching way to the pile of onions at the end of the aisle and pick out three. That was my assignment should I choose to take it. Fine. It wouldn't be pretty, but surely I could pick out three onions and put them in a plastic bag. You'd think so, huh?

I tried to navigate the crowded aisle without inflicting injury on innocent children or adults. The cart wasn't cooperating. It was an obvious struggle and I wasn't in the mood to grin and bear it. Before continuing this story, you need to know that anywhere I go I get curious stares — especially from children. I am obviously and distinctly handicapped. Usually, adults take quick glances and either smile some encouragement to me, or quickly look away to cover their curiosity and spare me embarrassment. Children on the other hand, just plain stare. I'm quite used to this and usually enjoy interacting with the curious ones. But not that night. I was stuck with a rebellious cart and a rebellious attitude. I was totally self-absorbed and darkly determined to complete my one and only shopping task. It seemed that others just didn't matter. I simply had to get to the onions. Eye straight ahead, I rudely carried on.

After running the gauntlet of curious eyes and completing the obstacle course of Aisle 3B, I arrived at my marked goal: the onions. I could smell the stinking pile way before I arrived to survey it. It had taken all I could muster to make it this far. The seeds of failure, frustration, and fury that had begun at home came into full bloom as I leaned on my cart in front of a pile of smelly, rotten onions. Strangely, I was all alone as I glared at the pathetic pile. Maybe others could sense I was about to hit the fan and had backed away to give me room to either implode or explode. Fear entered my mind when I realized how deep a hold fury had on me. I was ready to bust up the store. Growling and gritting my teeth I began to methodically pick up an onion and throw it back on the pile … one at a time. Pick it up and throw it back … one at a time. A couple hit the floor, but I didn't care. The onions were particularly large and over-ripe, the size of grapefruits. At some point in this simmering fury, I turned from the pile with the thought that it would be immensely satisfying to launch one of those big stinkers from Aisle 3B to Aisle 7B. I mean it. I was ready to launch!

I had one particularly large rotting onion in my right hand. With my left hand clutching the handhold of the cart I tried to fight the overpowering urge to commence count down. Out of nowhere, I felt a hand tap my left shoulder. The woman who had tapped me came around and stood flat in front of me. She was smiling. She had no idea how close she was to violence. Putting her face close to mine, she asked, "Is that black lens over your right eye permanent?" — What? *What!?*— My temper tantrum abruptly interrupted, it took a few seconds to get reoriented. I answered with grim finality, "Yes. I'm essentially blind in that eye." I was still holding the large potential projectile, but she didn't seem to notice. She unflinchingly continued, "So, you still have vision in your left eye?" Who is this? What does she want? I gave her a very grudging, "Yes," and started to turn away. She dared to put her hand on mine and said with great exuberance, "Count your blessings!" What? *What!?*

This encounter was so unusual that I got the notion that God could be up to something. But I stubbornly pushed Him away and attempted to do the same with her. But she kept coming at me. She told me that just a few days ago one of her best friends was hit by a car and as a result was now blind in both eyes. How blessed I was to still have vision in one eye. Then she admitted she was a bit confused concerning the anger her friend was experiencing, as this friend tried to adapt to being blind. I wasn't confused and I wasn't very nice either. I could have helped this woman understand her hurting friend, but I was too hung up in my own fury to be of any assistance. She threw me a huge, sweet smile and kept on shopping. I knew God had intervened at a crucial time in my petty, private rage. I dropped the big stinker back on the pile but I wasn't done with my anger yet. I found Jim and told him of this encounter. I even told him I thought God was trying to tell me something, but I wasn't ready to listen. Jim listened and kept quiet. Smart man; he knows how to handle volatile situations. Needless to say, we purchased no onions that night.

As we waited in the long checkout lines, complete with malfunctioning cash registers, tired shoppers and wailing children, I tried to come up out of my blue funk. But I was still ticked at my pathetic predicament. I was too weak and tired physically to be of any help to Jim as he bagged the groceries he had picked up while I'd been contemplating the murder of many rotten onions. So I just glumly hung on to the cart handle and listlessly watched him load our purchases. At one point I glanced up and looked over at the long line of shoppers waiting to check out to my left. As I did, another woman looked very sweetly at me and shyly smiled a greeting. I managed a weak smile back at her — my first of the night. I was right about God. He was up to something and He wasn't done with me yet.

I continued to wait for Jim to bag and load the groceries. The next time I looked up this other woman was standing next to me. I'll never forget her words: "I'm drawn to you." I just looked at her with my one blessed eye and tried to smile. She looked fragile, tired, and strangely familiar. She asked if I had ever spoken in churches about how to deal with physical disabilities. Meekly I replied, "Yes." She went on to say she'd heard me speak about a year before and she told me how helpful it had been for her. Oh man, God definitely had my attention now. Inside, I completely melted as I heard her story of a son in the hospital with cancer and her on-going personal battle with cancer. As I listened with a humbled spirit, my heart broke for her. My own failures, frustrations, furies, fears and finality were forgotten as I poured my attention onto another in more trouble than my selfish little self. She was sweet and compassionate and complimentary of me. I did not deserve such treatment; especially not that night.

God had placed two women directly in my path on the Night of the Rotten Onion Episode. He had purposed such a night and allowed me to pitch my fit for all to see. He wanted to teach me something important — something of value to never forget. I know what He wanted me to learn so I could help myself as well as others. Pamela, you must journal in your *Facing It Journal* daily. Daily. Don't try to do without it.

Journaling in my *Facing It Journal* is the only way to know where I stand in my Reactions to Disability. It is the only way to see the patterns of my reactions, choices and attitudes so I won't crash and burn. I am not immune to what I have written in this book called *FACING IT*. In order to

FACE my disabilities well I must journal, daily. It is essential to my well being and the well being of others.

I've told you, dear readers, this true confession at the beginning of this book so you will know with certainty that daily journaling is essential to FACING IT. And so you will know to take caution and stand clear if you bump into me near an onion pile.

 ## DARE – Handicappers

The DARE here, of course, is to begin a daily record of your own. Remember, this doesn't have to be Shakespeare! Tailor your journal to fit who you are. But I really think it is necessary for us handicappers to keep a record of our daily experiences and our reactions to them. I DARE you to begin FACING IT in writing. This will help clear the way for you to begin FACING IT physically, mentally, emotionally and spiritually. There is a *Facing It Journal* available to assist you in your daily writing. (More details are available at the FACING IT website: www.facingit.org.) Or, if you want to, create your own unique journaling system. You are one of a kind! I'll help you. Keep reading!

 ## DARE – Caregivers

Caregivers, I DARE you to especially note the experiences your capper is having, and how they're reacting to them. And it's equally important to record how you're reacting to them. You have a lot to FACE too, as one who has to look on and somehow try to help your capper handle life in the slow lane. In my opinion, journaling is essential in this process. A journal is a safe place to identify your own 5 Fs of Reaction to Physical Disability. The *Facing It Journal* is available to you, as a caregiver as well, if you want to use it. Or, you too can be creative and come up with your own style of journaling. But, the DARE is on! Journal daily. I'll help you. Keep reading!

Your journaling will involve not only your reactions to the 5 Fs, but also how you observe your capper handling them. Your journaling will also take into account how you are handling the BIG D, and how your capper is doing for that day. And your journaling will also involve how you are doing with the 4 good Fs and how your capper is doing as well. This really is a DOUBLE DARE for you caregivers. But I assure you; it is worth the time and effort — for both you and your capper. Remember, you can be brief, creative, and actually have some fun journaling. It doesn't have to become burdensome, but should be burden lifting. And I know you caregivers need to dump some of the burdens you carry for yourselves as well as for us cappers. Daily journaling will help you and your capper FACE IT.

Handicappers and Caregivers

The help is here! Handicappers and Caregivers get ready to receive some beneficial tips for journaling your way through disability. First of all, we need to realize that journaling is a personal, active, helpful way to process and evaluate all aspects of our lives. As such, journaling is a valuable tool to assist us in our daily dealings with physical disabilities. OK. Here comes the help.

1. **Commit to a routine.** Commit yourself to daily journaling. Are you ready to commit to this? Yes or no? No maybes here. I hope you're saying, "Yes!"

2. **Set a time to journal.** Do you want to begin each day with your personal observations, feelings, reactions, etc., or do you want to do this mid-day or evening? What works best for you? This timing issue may take some working out. Some trial and error. That's OK. This experience is very unique to each handicapper and caregiver. Sometimes I even like to mix it up and journal in the mornings some days, and in the evenings on other days. A lot depends on how I'm reacting to my disabilities on any given day. But, and this is a big but, continue to journal daily. Make it a priority. Whenever I miss several days in a row (oh yeah, it happens, remember the Rotten Onion Episode?) I pay a price. And it is costly. I lose immediate touch with just exactly where I am in my daily dealings with my physical handicaps. This puts me at real risk of being hurt by the rough ride of the 5 Fs of Reaction to Disability and I can slide, unaware, into the clutches of the Big D. I don't want to go there, and daily journaling helps me see which direction I'm heading, so I have some control and can make some deliberate choices. I like control. And daily journaling helps me to be in control as much as possible. I can see where I am and where I'm likely to end up. So, set a time to journal every day. And if you miss several days in a row, don't give up. Simply return to your journal and keep on keeping on. This is a huge benefit to your daily life. I know.

3. **Begin at the beginning.** What do I mean by this? Well, by the end of this handbook, you will be equipped to quickly (yes, I said quickly) journal with insight and skill on: all of the 5 Fs of Reaction to Disability, The BIG D, and the 4 Fs of Choice. You'll also learn about the Essentials at the top of the page and "My Box" at the bottom. We aren't there yet. We are just beginning.

   For now, whether handicapper or caregiver, begin to get in touch with your feelings, observations, and thoughts, as you FACE daily experiences with each other. Write something about what you discover. Keep it simple. Just begin. It is a start. A good start. It will get easier and become more natural, given time and effort. As handicappers and caregivers, you will be responding in active, helpful, personal ways to the human Reactions of Physical Disability. That's good.

4. **Create your own journal or make use of the *Facing It Journal*.** I do urge you to be creative, but it may help you to at least take a look at the journal lay out that I use. The Preface and Introduction of the *Facing It Journal* may help you create your own journal. Take a peek and go for your own creation, or simply pick up the *Facing It Journal* and begin. I know I need the imposed discipline of a journal with fill-in-the-blank daily pages. (I like to cross things off and literally see I have accomplished something during my day. Hence, the daily journal pages awaiting my pen.) Do what works best for you, but I encourage you to look at the format so useful to me. (Feel free to look. At no cost, and no obligation. If the journal isn't available where you purchased this book, then go online to www.facingit.org, for a sample.) If you do choose to use the *Facing It Journal*, I still want you to begin, for now, by only writing in the space titled "My Box." Make sure you read the Preface and the Introduction before you proceed in your *Facing It Journal*. Whatever your choice, I encourage you to journal daily. This is your mission, should you choose to accept it. Write!

Looking ahead. Whether you're put out about the idea of journaling every day, or you're ready to jump ahead and journal about everything, remember my tip to "begin at the beginning." As you proceed through this handbook you will learn to rank yourself daily on a scale of 0-10 for all of the 5 Fs of Reaction to Disability, and the BIG D. This is like a pain chart at the doctor's office — zero is great and 10 is miserable. If I'm at a 2 ranking for the day in any given F of Reaction, I know I'm doing pretty well in that area. But if I rate myself at 9, I know I need to be on red-alert and begin making quick and appropriate Good Choices to counter this potential downer, or the BIG D will grab me. Together, we'll build this skill one step at a time.

Ready to Ride

I think we're safely on board our roller coaster car now. I can feel an upward lurch as the gears engage and we jolt forward. The first of the 5 Fs of Reaction to Physical Disability we're going to look at is FAILURE. Oh, boy.

Chapter 1

The 5 Fs of Reaction to Disability:
FAILURE

> FAILURE – Definition: lack of success; omission of expected or required action; lack or deficiency of a desirable quality; action or state of not functioning.

FAILURE. What a crummy word; and an even crummier experience. If you are FACING a physical disability in your life, you've probably experienced FAILURE to some degree. I simply cannot make my body do some of the things it used to do so easily and automatically. This body is FAILING me. Tough, but true for me and my caregivers. I don't know what you are FACING, but the multiple physical FAILURES I FACE every day can really wear me down. I have lost personal independence in my every day life. Bummer. Big time bummer. So, what to DO, DON'T and DARE concerning these awful physical FAILINGS?

DO – Handicappers

DO begin to journal about FAILURE. (It didn't take long to get here, did it?) Identify the ways your body is FAILING you and how you feel about these FAILURES. Be brave. This is hard to FACE, but it seems to be a necessary part of acknowledging and accepting physical handicaps. Honestly assess losses, setbacks, and injuries. Enlist others to help you evaluate where your body is FAILING to operate normally and write down their observations too. These others may be family, friends, doctors, nurses, or therapists and their input is valuable to your realistic conclusion concerning your own body's FAILURES.

So now, let's add your thoughts about FAILURE to your daily journal. Use a scale of 0–10 and rank how you feel in this area each day. Begin to get in touch with your feelings, observations, and thoughts. Write them down as you FACE the various FAILURES of your body. Be consistent, and write something every day. (If you're using the *Facing It Journal*, there's a spot to record your numeric rank, and describe your reactions, next to the word FAILURE.)

How do you feel about keeping a written record of how your body is FAILING you every day? (Probably about as good as I feel about it!) Please write your reactions to this DO, now.

DO – Caregivers

You too, Caregivers. Please DO begin to journal about FAILURE, from your point of view. Please note that the instructions for the handicappers apply to you as well. DO your ranking from 0–10. Don't forget that when you're recording your reactions to FAILURE, you need to consider both your own *and* your capper's reactions. How does your capper's sense of FAILURE affect you? Do you feel like you're FAILING because you're unable to change the physical conditions your capper deals with? Do you feel like you have FAILED to provide the care they need? Here's a box for you to write about FAILURE today in this handbook, but start journaling too.

 ## DON'T – Readers

DON'T ignore this essential DO. Staring FAILURE in the FACE may be rough. Writing about it may be even harder. DON'T forget you can take advantage of the *Facing It Journal*, and keep the writing to a minimum, while still recording the essential information — how well am I FACING FAILURE today?

 **DARE – Readers**

The DARE here is to commit to a daily record of your life, recording the ways in which, as handicappers, our bodies are FAILING us, and how this affects our pursuit of life, liberty, and happiness. The DARE for you caregivers is to pay attention to the ways in which your capper's body is FAILING, and how this affects your pursuit of life, liberty, and happiness. I DARE you to be brave enough to assist your capper in ways most needed as you watch their bodies FAIL. DARE to be brave, and speak the truth in love to your capper, as you track their FAILINGS in your journal.

DO – Handicappers

DO encourage your caregiver to journal their observations and feelings as they watch your body FAIL. This is hard.

 ### DO – Caregivers

DO encourage your capper to journal their observations and feelings as their bodies FAIL them. This is hard.

 ### DON'T – Handicappers

DON'T try to ignore the ways in which your body is failing you. Denial gets old and eventually impossible anyway. FACING IT head on in your journaling helps you immediately begin to deal with the physical challenges and changes in your life. Journaling helps you learn your true physical limitations and places where you might be able to stretch and challenge your body. Seeing your physical condition as it really is takes guts and time. It is worth recording your own unique observations, emotions, and conclusions. Trust me.

 ### DON'T – Caregivers

It might be a temptation on your part to downplay or discount the obvious physical setbacks of one you love. DON'T. The handicapper needs to have a reliable source of factual information concerning the FAILING parts of their bodies. Of course hugs, kisses, flowers, cards, and other special ways of saying, "I care," don't hurt! Journaling will assist you to assist them and help you as you deal with FAILURE.

 **DARE – Readers**

One last time, I DARE you to begin or to continue your daily record. I DARE you to overcome the inevitable barriers to journaling — lack of time, lack of desire, fatigue, denial, procrastination, laziness, and inertia — and FACE IT in writing!

Okay. I'll be honest with you. Even though I kept an accurate, but minimal journal over the last 9 years, I did not begin my Facing It Journal until well into the writing of this book. You already know I struggle with the writing down of details. But, the very day I took on the DARE to begin to specifically use my Facing It Journal, I saw the immense benefits of briefly detailing my daily situation as a handicapper. And I have continued in this practice. There is something very beneficial about writing down what I am experiencing in the 5 Fs, the BIG D, and the 4 Fs. I can hardly believe it. But it's true. This brief, creative, often humorous, sometimes hideously sobering daily assessment of just where I am in these specific areas of my life really helps me FACE my handicaps better. Cool. And maybe you even like to write. Even cooler.

DO – Handicappers

DO allow others to help you when you know you need it. Ouch! This one is still hard for me. I want to be totally independent even when I know it is impossible. DO let family, friends, and even strangers help, when you need it. Eventually, hopefully, we will all reach that place where we can cheerfully ask for help when we need it.

> I need help from other people all the time. This has been a major adjustment, obviously. I'll never forget the very first time I was really confronted by someone on this touchy issue of needing help vs. independence. At the time, I was still able to drive and I had just parked our car in the church parking lot. It was a pretty Wednesday morning and I was looking forward to meeting with many women for our regular Bible study. As a leader, I had a lot of stuff to carry from the car, to the church, to the room where our group met. I was struggling to balance my load of books, papers, folders, purse and the ever-present bag of emergency diabetes supplies, when a good friend came up along side of me and asked, "May I help?"
>
> You already know my answer. With, I'm assuming, a lovely, valiant, quite independent Princess smile, I sweetly replied, "No. I'm fine." She persisted with, "May I help you?" at least three times more as I struggled to walk towards the building. Then she literally stopped me in my tracks. Looked me straight in the eyes (she has beautiful brown ones) and said, "Would you rob me of the blessing of helping you, my dear friend?" How do you answer that one? I melted. All my pride and doggedly determined struggle for continued independence fell away. I did need help and she knew how to help me acknowledge that fact. With a sheepish grin, I gave in to my need and her gracious help. She thanked me and I thanked her.
>
> I learned valuable lessons that morning. At times I simply need help. I need to let others help me when I need it. This will give them pleasure and assist me at the same time. And, the person needing help and the one helping, are drawn together in a special bond of relationship, whether friend or stranger. So, now, after 5 years of practice, I mostly enjoy

> *asking others to help me when I need it. Mostly. Often it is strangers. Often it involves restrooms. You can really bond with someone in that situation. I think you get the point.*

Is it hard for you to ask for help? Which situations are the hardest? How do you feel about this touchy issue? Please write below.

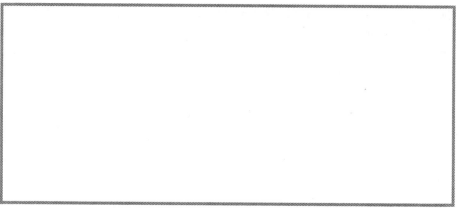

 ## DO – Caregivers

DO, by **careful** trial and error, learn when to offer help and when not to. This is tricky and you can expect several, if not many, flare-ups from your handicapper as you both learn to adjust to the handicapper's physical failures, limitations, and lack of independence. DO ask your handicapper to show you how to best help them in common and uncommon circumstances. How does your capper respond to offers of physical assistance? How does this make you feel? Now it's your turn to write.

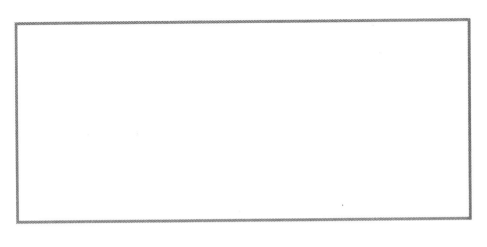

 DON'T – Handicappers

DON'T let your natural desire for independence keep you from graciously asking and accepting the help you need, when you need it. I'm talking to myself here, too. DON'T let pride keep you from allowing others to give you what they can — help and assistance when necessary. DON'T prevent the double blessing of letting another help you. Please DON'T.

> *I was having difficulty negotiating the entrance to a supermarket door. Two of the toughest, biggest, roughest, dirtiest young men I've ever encountered, came up beside me. In my tiny, little, limited mind, I thought, "Yikes!" One of the young men approached me and ever so sweetly asked if I needed help in the door. "Yes, please," I meekly replied. They proceeded to carefully maneuver around me and the grocery cart I was using for support, and held the door wide open, for a humbled Princess Pam. With huge smiles on their faces, they thanked me, before I could thank them! A bond of companionship was somehow formed, and I will never forget their kindness, eagerness and gratefulness to be of help to this spazzy handicapper. We all would have missed out on that "random act of kindness", had I simply reacted in pride and fear and said, "No."*

Has anything like that ever happened to you? Did you say "yes" or "no" to the help offered? Have you ever felt the sweet bond of friendship with strangers, simply by allowing them to help you? Take time to remember and write.

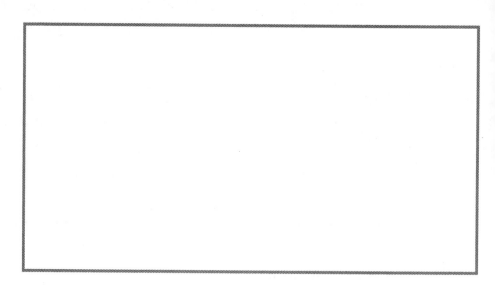

 DON'T – Caregivers

This is a tricky DON'T for you. You are going to have to feel your way carefully in this area of independence versus the need for help, for your capper. But DON'T allow your capper to develop a hard attitude of rejection of help when help is needed. You know them better than anyone. Help them not to say, "No," to offers of assistance when needed. This will almost certainly be draining on you and on them. Hey, I'm the handicapper here, not the caregiver. This DON'T is yours to figure out. Good luck. I mean it nicely. How can you help your capper accept help? Do you, as a caregiver, need help? Please think about it and write.

 DARE – Handicappers

DARE to seek the limits of your physical independence. *Safely* push the edges of your physical limitations. I said, "Safely." DARE to do whatever it takes to experience the largest degree of physical independence you can. Realize you risk personal disappointment as well as possible reward. DARE to be prepared for either. The roller coaster is rolling!

I've gotta set you up for this one. We've lived in Portland, Oregon, for 29 years. We love this place. As you may or may not know, it rains a lot here. Like from November through May. (Ok, that's a slight exaggeration.) Today, as I write to you, it is the second day of Spring Break, a Tuesday. It hasn't rained for two days straight. It is beautiful outside. Trees are budding, flowers are blooming, the pollen count is off the charts, and our gorgeous, green, Oregon grass is growing so fast and so tall, I think I can hear it pushing skyward. I want to mow. I love to mow. I haven't mowed the grass in over 3 years, but today I want to try. I woke up planning my day around a possible attempt to mow. (Remember, I said to safely test the limits of your physical abilities? Now I have to listen to my own typing!)

I did a very wise thing, but only because I had to. I know I can't get to the mower or start the mower by myself, so I asked my darling husband if he would help me. When I mentioned that I wanted to try to mow our fresh, new, spring grass, he looked at me as if I'd just asked him if I could go bungee jumping off Multnomah Falls. He said, "No." A man of direct communication, I had no questions, just complaints.

When I mentioned my intention to mow to our oldest daughter, she laughed. She has a dark sense of humor. When I mentioned it to our middle daughter, her practical reply was that it would be smarter to wait until someone else had completed the 1st mow of the season, so I wouldn't be defeated by 10 inch grass and a blown mower engine. She also pointed out a road trip we were planning for the next day, and that I would probably be very sorry to have mowed today. (Riding in the car wrapped in ice and sucking down aspirin didn't sound appealing, even to me.) When I mentioned my intention to our youngest daughter, she soberly said, "Just don't fall in front of the blade, Ma."

I'm hearing them. I'm not so happy with this FAILING body, but they are right ... for today. For today, the safest thing I can do is not to stretch the DARE too far. I've heard from all 4 of my primary caregivers, and I choose to listen to their advice. I love a good DARE, and you probably know as well as I do, sometime this spring, I will attempt a mow. If only someone will start the mower and get me out to it.

Are you willing to *safely* DARE to experience the largest degree of physical independence possible for you? What are you thinking?

 DARE – Caregivers

DARE to help your handicapper seek the limits of their physical disabilities. *Safely.* Some handicappers may be chomping at the bit to test themselves, and others may need coaxing to even begin to move toward an exploration of the borders of dependence on others. DARE to help them DARE a little bit. *Safely.* DARE to be prepared to cheer them up and on, if disappointed. DARE to challenge them to keep keeping on safely testing their physical limitations no matter what. Even some tiny degree of experienced physical independence is immensely preferable to none. I know.

> *I just want to talk about jumping. Me ... jumping. If you want a laugh, just watch me try to jump. When I suggested my family watch me try this at a fun, family gathering, they all began shaking their heads, groaning, frowning and giving me the please-don't-do-something-stupid look. I receive this look a lot, so it didn't faze me. I tried jumping anyway. If I could just show you now, how pathetic and funny this looks, I would. I DARED to be safely dumb and my family grudgingly allowed me. (Walls were close enough to hold on to if needed.) I jumped with all the might this body could muster. I managed to reach maybe ¼ inch off of the floor. We all laughed so hard, I had to "run" to the bathroom, producing more*

> *laughter. It was a safe DARE I wanted to try, and the laughter was well worth the effort.*

Caregivers, how do you feel about urging your capper to safely push the limits of their physical disabilities? What are some ways to gently persuade your adventuresome capper to hold back a bit for safety's sake? (Good humor can be invaluable in these situations.) Please write your thoughts about pushing the limits and holding back.

DO – Handicappers

DO allow others to laugh at and with you. DO be prepared for open mouthed stares of children and minimally disguised sidelong glances of adults. DO practice an easy, open, friendly, simple explanation of your apparent physical problems. DO encourage an open dialogue with others. It's liberating and fun once you get used to it. DO realize that this process will take patience, practice and a humble acceptance of what we look like to the world at large. DO help put others at ease by a conscious, practiced effort on your part. DO allow humor to invade all levels of your being: physical, mental, emotional, and spiritual. Laugh. Enjoy. DO it to the best of your ability. This will be easier for some of you and harder for others. Give these DOs a try!

> *Since I have one black lens and one clear lens on my glasses (look at the back cover of this book), little girls and boys around the ages of three to five years old, are convinced that I am some sort of a Disney character that somehow escaped the park. I get everything from shy smiles and little waves, to exclamations of glee and wild hoots, depending on the child, and how quickly the mom or dad swoops down to stifle their joy. The term pirate abounds. I usually put on a sweet smile (even if I don't feel like smiling) and wave back at them with my best professional Disney character impersonation.*
>
> *Often, I need to openly respond to straightforward questions from children and adults. You can guess which questions are usually from kids and which are usually from adults: "Are you really a pirate?" No, with a big smile. "Are you blind in that eye?" Not really blind, but it just doesn't work right. "What is wrong with you?" How much time do you have? "What's behind the black glass?" Would you like to see? Being Princess Pam, I enjoy all this attention and interaction, even though I don't particularly enjoy the reasons for it. I DO hope as a handicapper, you can get comfortable with how you look physically and can help others get comfortable too.*

Do you want to review the list of DOs and try some out? Write down some DOs you could try out, and then DO them.

 DO – Caregivers

DO help your handicapper begin to endure and hopefully at some point, even enjoy the stares of children and attention of adults. Humor is the key here. So I hope you have a good sense of one. Laughter at your shared situation can defuse a potential downer. Use it as well as you can, knowing the funny bones of your own handicapper. If they are unusually self-conscious about their appearance, try to help them ease up a bit. If they seem to need help, DO help them formulate a simple explanation of their handicap, so they can gracefully and quickly extricate themselves from prying questions and eyes, if necessary. Help them begin to laugh with you at themselves and this incredibly powerless place they're in. When things start to get funny, I think they start to somehow get better.

There are many in our church who are caregivers to me. One of my favorites was absolutely indispensable to my well-being, when everything fell apart for me in the summer of 1999. He was our Sunday school teacher for years as well as Pastor of Adult Education and Family Ministries, and a friend. When I first had to start using a cane to maneuver this body around, I was very self-conscious, even for a Princess.

I thought it made me look old (I was only 51) and I didn't like it. The very first Sunday I showed up at Sunday school with this horrid cane, one girl friend said she thought I looked sexy. That was a good start. She meant it!

This pastor/teacher then proceeded to tease me, as only he could, with a class of 40 people looking on. He called me Yoda. Yep, Yoda. If you are familiar with the original Star Wars movies, you'll know why he called me Yoda. (If not, Yoda is a small, wrinkled, Jedi Master, who wields a cane.) He made me laugh at myself then and there and I came to love his nickname for me. Some in class were horrified at this name-calling, but later saw it helped me. He has since moved to another state to pastor his own church and I so miss his knowing ways of making me comfortable with my handicaps. I miss being called Yoda by my friend and Bible teacher. As you're reading this, will you just whisper the name, Yoda, and think of me? Thanks.

Please look back over the list of DOs and write down how you might use humor to help your capper.

45

DON'T – Handicappers

DON'T take your physical disabilities too seriously. DON'T stay away from other people out of fear of their reactions to how you look or move. DON'T exclude yourself from the lives of others, or others from your life. DON'T lose your sense of humor. DON'T let your physical handicaps rule you. DON'T.

How are you responding to these DON'Ts?

 DON'T – Caregivers

DON'T let your capper get away with murder. I mean this. It is almost suicide, murder of a kind, to remove oneself from others, because of self-consciousness connected to disability. DON'T let your capper keep away from others. DON'T let them kill whatever humor is possible, for them, and for you, and for others. You may have to really work hard on this DON'T, but it is so necessary for your well-being as well as your capper's.

What might be some good ways to work on these DON'Ts?

 DARE – Handicappers

DARE to put yourself in the public eye! If possible, go to the mall, ride a bus, shop for food, go to the zoo, go to the movies, go to your place of worship. Get seen! Step out and enjoy whatever level of independence is possible for you. DARE to notice curious children and smile and wave at them, if you are able. Meet the eyes of those around you and put them at ease. DARE to be exactly who you are. Wear your disabilities with dignity and grace. It is possible. Go ahead and take this DARE!

Are you ready? What will you DARE to do?

DARE – Caregivers

DARE to help place your handicapper in the public eye. DARE to take on the challenge of humor in the face of possible despair. There may be times of intense scrutiny that your handicapper just can't endure. Be ready to support them with a hug and some sweetened humor of your own. DARE to keep encouraging them to get out and about in the real world. DARE to do whatever it takes on your part, to get them out. DARE to sacrifice your time, your energy and your own emotions concerning their physical appearance and disabilities. DARE to be approachable and welcome other people to come close to both you and your handicapper. DARE to enjoy the attentions of others.

What do you think about these DAREs?

DO – Handicappers

This DO is very specific. I learned this one first hand not too long ago. DO go to a live physical event. Any questions? Here's what happened to me so you'll be in the know: I hadn't been to a live physical event for years. Both of our younger daughters played basketball from fifth grade through high school, so in my pre-handicapped days my husband and I were on overload concerning exciting, physical exhibitions. But our girls are all grown up now and it had been ages since we'd attended any kind of live event that involved physical activity.

We were given tickets to go see a live performance of Cirque de Soleil and we were thrilled at the opportunity. I had no idea how profound an experience this would be for me at this point in my life. As you can imagine, having virtually no mobility in my legs makes for a sedentary lifestyle — very ho hum. So, sitting in some very choice seats at the Cirque, I could hardly wait for the show to begin. And *pow*! It began.

At the "halftime" (remember our girls were in basketball) I was flushed and bubbling with joy. It only took me a moment to figure out why … the immense physical prowess being displayed so beautifully and so close to me, made **me** feel powerful as well. This may be hard to understand, but try it.

DO go to a live physical event. Go to a basketball game, a ballet performance, a wrestling match, a track meet, a football game, or a kung fu competition. Your choices are endless. Choose a specific physical event and see. I got lost in the midst of the intense physical nature of the performance, and it was wonderful, freeing and fun. DO try it.

I just can't pass up another example of this watch-a-live-physical-event-and-feel-empowered-phenomenon. This one was exciting, intense, suspenseful, very up close and very personal.

My husband has worked for many years with a bright, unique, personable, multi-talented woman. They do something with computers. She is quite lovely; petite, at 5' 2", with beautiful, long, soft brown hair, and eyes of changing colors. Who would think she could knock your block off if she wanted to? Besides being quite brainy, she's quite brawny, and it was our privilege to be invited to watch her attempt to acquire her black belt in karate. Realize now, that we care for Irena (her name means "peace") and she was about to be in the fight of her life.

As we arrived, the small gym was packed with people invited to watch the participants attempt to demonstrate that they were ready for a special colored belt. Black is the highest level to be attained. Many other colored belts must be acquired and skills proven, before one takes on the black belt challenge. As we spectators lined the walls of the mirrored gym, we watched many try to get whatever color was up next for them. Some failed and that was painful, even for the spectators. Some succeeded, and that was rewarding, even for the spectators.

The people trying for black belts went last of all, and our expectations were sky high as we anticipated Irena's upcoming test of skill and endurance. At least an hour had passed as we watched many other karate students try to attain their goals. As observers, we were now as hot and sweaty as the participants, and our adrenalin levels were as high as physically possible for those sitting in chairs or on the floor. I was sitting on my red walker, jammed next to Irena's husband and young son and my own husband. Then, in the confines of this close, hot, old gym, it was Irena's turn to prove herself worthy of a black belt. (My heart beats faster right now, just remembering this experience.)

First, she was put through a rigorous round of special exercises that would have killed me on a good day at age 21. Next, she was surrounded by eight people. They encircled her, and attacked her constantly, in many different ways. She was so quick and accomplished. I was holding my breath. She seemed to do well in my eyes. Then it was time for the final test of her ability. She had to go one on one with an accomplished black belt, and do well enough to earn her own, or fail trying.

50

I had to remind myself to breathe. By now, she was tired and flushed, her beautiful, braided hair was coming undone, and I was scared for her. (I was perched on the edge of my walker, yet I felt like it was almost me, who would have to FACE this last physical test.) She was called to the center of the gym and her opponent was called out to FACE her. His nickname, behind his back, was Godzilla. The nickname fit. He looked like he could stomp on villages and send screaming crowds through city streets. He was tall, at least 250 pounds, and a professional trainer and fighter. I saw fear flash briefly in Irena's eyes as she FACED him straight on and bowed. I was scared to death for her. The only prayer my brain could muster was, "God, help her."

It began, and it wasn't pretty. It was rough and tough — a true contest of wills and skills. By the way, the spectators were to remain silent throughout all of the contests we observed. This is the acceptable protocol in such situations. I'd been able to be fairly quiet up until our Irena's test.

As you know by now, just in general it is difficult for me to be quiet. Uh, oh! Blows were landing hard and fast on both Irena and her opponent. My hands were over my mouth on purpose. But when Godzilla threw her, flat on her back, hard to the floor, I let out an "ahhhh" that received frowns from all around and a punch in the ribs from my husband. I hurt for her, but she leapt to her feet and continued on. At the end of what seemed like a decade of blows and throws, the contest was over. Godzilla had met his match. Our little Irena had held her own and was awarded her black belt in karate. Wow! In the thick of it, she had even drawn a little blood from the professional, black belt master, who was quite graciously and truly congratulating her. The room exploded in applause and I imploded with relief and joy.

I hadn't lifted a finger in defense or offense, but I was pleasantly worn out and exuberant from her physical prowess. It was so good for this handicapper to experience up close and personal, this highly charged, physical event. We had a party afterward. Our personal connection with Irena elevated all my responses to the physical action. I'm pumped, just typing out this fun memory of Irena's black belt competition!

DO get out and experience physical events. Think of something you could go to, see, and experience, and then follow through. DO it!

Where can you go? What would you like to experience?

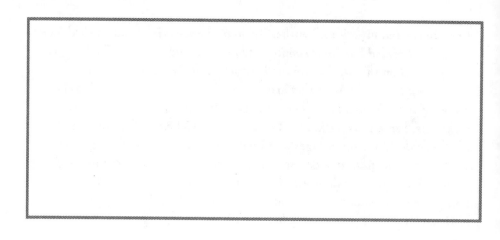

 DO – Caregivers

DO whatever it takes to get your handicapper to a live physical event! Save your money for tickets. Be on the lookout for special events coming to town. Go with a group to get a better deal on group ticket prices. DO make sure the event you plan to attend has handicap access and seating. Sometimes these are the best seats in the house. A perk for you and your capper. There are cheap thrills in most towns too: high school, middle school, or even elementary school competitions can be a blast, whether you know someone on the team or not. DO get you and your capper out. Where can you go? What would be fun to see?

 DON'T – Handicappers

DON'T settle for sitting on the couch and watching sports or action movies. That is way too passive. DON'T settle for listening to the radio. If at all possible DON'T settle into your little comfort zone. DON'T be afraid to get out and get close to the real arena of physical action. Even if you can't move well, like me, you will be energized by the up-close physical activities of others.

DON'T settle for in-home passivity. DON'T.

Your response?

 **DON'T – Caregivers**

DON'T allow your capper to settle for the little, measured amounts of vicarious physical activity that TV and radio supply. DON'T you settle either! DON'T miss out on the incredible rush, flush, and excitement of up close, real physical events. DON'T.

Your response?

 DARE – Handicappers

I DARE you to forget what you look like and any physical FAILINGS that may be plaguing you and risk going out to a fun, physical event of your choice! I DARE you to fully immerse yourself in the strength, beauty and power that others can demonstrate. I DARE you to totally forget yourself and run, jump, twirl, slam dunk, fly through the air, skate, swim, run, sweat, and "be physical" with those actually participating in front of you! Yippee!

Will you DARE to try?

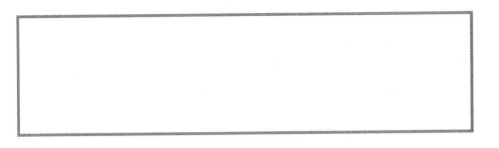

 DARE – Caregivers

I DARE you to help your capper forget themselves and their own physical FAILINGS. I DARE you to think of ways to accomplish this. I DARE you to think of unique physical situations you can place them in so they can enjoy this freeing experience. Think, and then go and have fun together!

What do you think?

DO – Handicappers

DO exercise. If at all possible, exercise daily. *Safely.* There are good videos available for all kinds of physically challenged people. There are classes at hospitals, gyms and community centers that are tailored for us spazzes and people with other physical disabilities. Many of us have good physical therapists who will create a special exercise regime just for us. There are even some adapted exercise programs on regular television. Look for these in your TV guide. But do exercise some part of your body — every day.

> I used to like going to the nearby community gym with a good friend. We'd talk and laugh and workout together, using weights, stationary bikes, treadmills, and all the other great equipment available. No more for me. It's been at least 6 years since we enjoyed perspiring together: she had babies and I got spazzed. But since the spaz years, I have personally come to know the immense value of exercising whatever I have left over from my handicaps. You'd probably get a good laugh watching me adapt my exercises to my favorite video workouts. But I am truly thankful to be able to do as much as I can. I hold onto a table with one hand for balance, and go for it with Leslie Sansone and her <u>Fat Burner Walk 2 Miles</u> in-home video and her <u>Walk the Walk</u> workout video.
>
> I know I have better balance, more strength, and more flexibility when I work out with Leslie. If I miss my regular routine with her, my body lets me know it in various painful and uncomfortable ways. Her fun workouts (only seventeen minutes to half an hour) benefit my spazzy body, and help to keep me faithful to regular, safe, in-home physical exercise. I agree with my video friend, Leslie. Regular exercise is essential to good physical, mental, emotional, and spiritual health.

I hope you're hearing me. Exercise is essential. I don't know what you are currently FACING, but please regularly move whatever you can, however you can.

What can you move? Will you move it regularly? Do you need help to begin or continue? Do you want to exercise?

 DO – Caregivers

DO encourage your capper to exercise. Now, this can be tricky. As you probably already know, it can be difficult, if not impossible, to make another person **want** to exercise. You will need to be tactful, charming, and persistent. It may stretch the limits of your relationship as well as their hamstrings. DO be ready for resistance for whatever reasons. But DO realize that moving with regularity any parts of their bodies that can still move is extremely important to physical, mental, emotional and spiritual health. DO help your capper toward this goal.

How can you help your capper with these DOs?

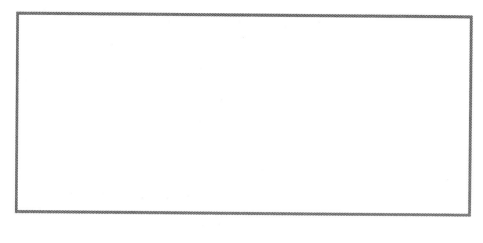

 ## DON'T – Handicappers

DON'T resist daily exercise. Resistance is futile. It's worse than futile. Without regular exercise of some sort, it is a fact that our bodies weaken, atrophy, and transform into sedentary blobs. You don't want a blob body and neither do I.

My poor husband! He has his own business and a home office in our second bedroom. We have a small house. I clomp all over the house as much as possible. And I mean clomp. Because of my spazzy legs, I kind of drag my feet when I walk. And because of the inflexibility of my legs, wearing clogs is the only way to go — I don't have to try to tie and untie shoelaces. Can you hear the clomp, drag, clomp, drag?

About 2 years ago, our middle daughter had a great idea. Wear a step-counting pedometer, and attempt the goal of 10,000 steps each day. And so I do. I do it inside the house mostly, unless someone is available to help me walk outside (if it isn't raining), or take me to the mall or to the market. Usually, I am attempting my daily 10,000 steps inside the house, with my hardworking husband just about 20 steps away (I've counted it out).

Sometimes it gets to him. I can understand. But he is a kind and patient man and leaves me undisturbed to pace and clomp while on the cordless phone, waiting for laundry to spin, or tea water to get hot in the micro-wave. There are endless possibilities for clomping. The pedometer gives me a set goal to try for and helps me keep moving, even though I'm

> *housebound. Can you hear me? Clomp, drag, clomp, drag, comp, drag. Jim*
> *isn't crazy ... yet.*

Please DON'T resist whatever level of physical exercise you can manage. Be creative. The payoff is worth it. Do you realize that resisting *safe* exercise is harmful to you? Are you willing to move whatever you can, whenever you can? Please write.

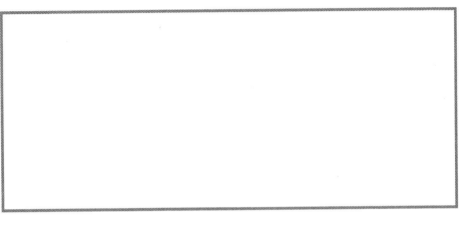

 DON'T – Caregivers

DON'T allow your capper to manipulate their way out of daily exercise. Whatever level they are capable of — keep them at it. Don't give up. Get smart. Don't allow excuses. Be creative. Use humor, rewards, and your own form of humane manipulation, keeping their best interest at heart. DON'T let your capper weasel out!

> *OK — more about my poor husband. I just can't resist the analogy that popped into my head as I awoke from my daily hour nap. (Napping is necessary for this video-exercising, multi-stepping, one-eyed writer, who would rather be talking.) The nap helps refresh this body and this easily fatigued blue-gray eye.*
>
> *Here's what I woke up thinking about, and laughing about. Not only is my husband kind and patient, he is brave and heroic. He's quite similar to the leading man in the old, black and white Alfred Hitchcock thriller, The 39 Steps. Get it? Steps! Clomp, drag. Clomp, drag. Clomp, drag.*

> *This movie was one of Alfred's favorites, because he thought, "the tempo was perfect." Get it? Tempo! Clomp, drag. Clomp, drag. Clomp, drag.*
>
> *This film is dubbed a suspense thriller, in which the leading man is "handcuffed to the girl that double-crossed him." I can't help but laugh. Everywhere we go, if I don't have my red walker with me, my dear husband must hold the hand of the "girl" whose body double-crossed him (and her). Thank God, in our case, we enjoy the "handcuffing."*

Maybe "handcuffing" is the only way you'll keep your capper from refusing to exercise every day. What do you think?

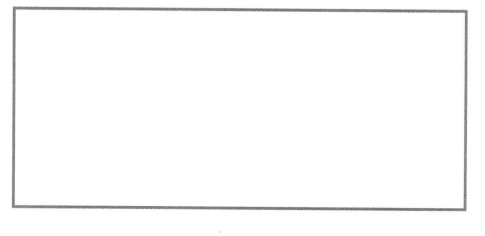

 DARE – Handicappers

DARE to be an extreme handicapper. *Safely* push the limits of your astounding physical prowess. Exercise with the best of the adapted exercise leaders. Hang out in the gym, if you can, or at the pool. At the pool? Yikes! That's a DARE for me too. The very thought of seeing this 56 year old body all alone in a dressing room mirror, is scary enough! But to be seen gimping along a slippery, wet pool deck, only to FACE the big machine that will lower me into the water, is daunting, even for this mostly confident Princess. But I need to take the DARE. I know I do. And I bet you know what exercise DARE you need to take as well. Go ahead. I DARE you to exercise however you can — regularly and safely. Even if this literally means trying to raise and lower your eyebrows five times a day. I'm not joking.

Are you ready to be an extreme handicapper? What can you *safely* DARE?

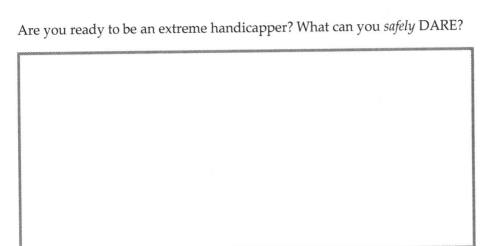

I'll be honest with you now, even though I don't want to. I haven't been swimming yet. There are many reasons why. None, however, are good enough. And I know it. Hopefully, before this book is completed, I'll have taken my own DARE. Be assured, I'll let you know when I manage to overcome all the reasons I shouldn't be in the water. I used to love to swim and dive. Somehow, I know I'll love the water once again, if I can just get past my self-conscious insecurities and physical handicaps. There are plenty of loving caregivers to help me. I'm just not ready quite yet. But soon?

(I told you I'd let you know. After writing, but before publishing, in the summer of 2005 I took the plunge. I tried swimming as my family looked on. It was wonderful. I didn't sink! It wasn't pretty, but I could move through the water. It felt like I was flying. I am <u>so</u> glad to know I can still swim!)

 DARE – Caregivers

Here's your DARE — I DARE you to be committed enough to your capper to "work out" with them — whatever that implies. If they need to walk a half a mile a day, go with them. If they have some basic, boring, physical therapy routines they need to go through each day, go through them together and somehow, have fun. If a swim 3 times a week is the way to go, go with them. I DARE you to encourage them by your own enthusiastic participation with them. You get it, don't you? Whatever the type or amount of exercise required for the capper's maximum benefit, I DARE you to go with them. It'll be good for both of you. You get another double DARE.

What do you think?

DO – Handicappers

DO be completely honest with your caregivers, doctors, and other health care professionals concerning all aspects of your health: physical, mental, emotional and spiritual. Since we are handicappers it is obvious that our bodies are FAILING us in observable ways. We know our bodies, minds and emotions better than anyone else, and we must be honest with our health care providers and caregivers at all times. Even when we don't want to admit to certain FAILINGS, we must. Even if we are uncomfortable and afraid to tell of further FAILINGS, we simply must FACE IT head on and tell others, what we don't even want to admit it to ourselves. This DO can be very hard to DO. I know.

> There is something I have to FACE every day now, that is still very embarrassing to me. I resisted telling my neurologist for months, even though every time I visited his office, he would ask me if I was having any problems in this area of my disability. I made a huge mistake by not informing my doctor when this problem first began. The official name for this physical FAILING is "incontinence."
>
> In laymen's terms, incontinence means, if you sneeze, cough, or laugh, and there is any urine in your bladder, you are in imminent danger of peeing your pants. There. I said it. How embarrassing. But true.
>
> I hid this from my family and doctor as best I could, until one day the dam burst, in a very obvious way. Our daughters and two grandchildren were visiting and we were all playing on the living room floor with toys. Like a 3-year old, I'd forgotten to go to the bathroom because of all the fun we were having. At home alone, I'd make sure to visit the place of porcelain at least every hour, for the sake of security and dry clothes. But, here I was, wrapped up in child's play with my dearest ones, and I'd neglected to note the time. I don't remember now what was said or done, but we all began to laugh together. And, oh no — I couldn't hold back! I was sitting on the living room carpet and I knew I had to make a mad rush to the bathroom, which was only about 20 clomp, drags away. But with spastic legs, to get up off the floor takes much effort, and, I didn't make it. In

front of my children and grandchildren I flooded my jeans and the carpet. I was horrified, embarrassed and humbled. I couldn't hide this problem any longer.

They all responded well to this surprising incident. They helped me up off the floor and then helped save my damaged Princess ego. After cleaning up and changing my clothes, I rather sheepishly re-entered the living room full of family. With humor and gentleness, they asked if I'd told the doctor about this problem. I had to answer, "No." They all agreed it was time to advise him of this latest development in my medical history. Well, fine! On my next regular appointment with my neurologist, I answered, "Yes," to the incontinence question, and told him of my recent problems. I should have spoken up months before, because he had a simple solution. He reduced the amount of a certain medication I took daily, greatly improving this potentially embarrassing area of my disability. I can still experience dangerously close "accidents" (and actual incidents), but I am much improved. So, see. Even though I was personally embarrassed to tell my doctor, and my family, I should have done so at the very start of this problem. I would have been helped immediately had I been forthcoming in this area. Sneaking and hiding my problem did me harm, not good.

DO, again I say, DO tell your health care professionals and your caregivers about any ongoing, current or new problems you are FACING. This embarrassing problem is better for me, for now, but not gone. So stand back if you catch me laughing out of control.

Is there something you need to tell your caregiver or health care professionals?

 **DO – Caregivers**

DO encourage your capper to be completely honest with you and with their healthcare professionals. Remember this is difficult for us at times, especially if we notice more FAILURES occurring in these already handicapped bodies. DO be on the lookout for us. Always pay close attention to details in the lives of your cappers. Notice any changes — physical, mental, emotional or spiritual — large changes or small changes, for better or for worse. DO be a devoted observer of your capper. You are more impartial than we are and may notice something important to our health care. Please DO communicate any changes you notice to your capper. Hopefully, they will take the information you give them to heart and allow your observations to help them understand what changes may be occurring in the midst of their disabilities. This may be difficult, but somehow, as the caregiver, figure out a way to help your capper come to grips with new developments you may notice. Help them to a place of acceptance and an ability to truthfully communicate new problems to you and to their health care professionals. DO realize this may not be quick or easy for you or for them.

Are you willing to be on the lookout for your capper? What do you see?

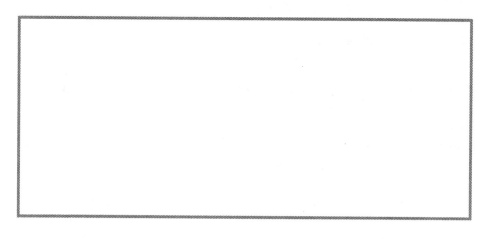

 DON'T – Handicappers

DON'T ignore, hide, or pretend away any new problems that arise on the thrilling horizon of your physical handicaps. As I've learned from experience, this does no good and may even cause harm.

> *This is another confession. Good grief. I am a slow learner. I knew I was physically weaker and way dizzier than I had been. Did I tell anyone? Of course not! Could my primary caregivers tell? Of course they could. Did they let me get away with pretending I wasn't any worse? No. So, once again, I had to fess up to my doctor. Once again, medication was adjusted and I functioned way better. Well, duh! DON'T try to hide the facts — period. Maybe you can be helped and maybe you can't. But it doesn't hurt (anything but your/my pride) to inform your primary caregivers and physicians.*

Are you trying to hide something? Please fess up.

 DON'T – Caregivers

DON'T let your capper get away with ignoring, hiding or pretending that new problems haven't intruded into an already crummy disability scenario. It is extremely hard for most cappers to admit to further problems in our lives. But please, DON'T let your capper deny reality and suffer further consequences. I know you will follow through on this one. It is so important to let honesty and good communication rule.

How can you kindly deal with this DON'T concerning your handicapper? Is there denial or hiding going on with your capper?

 **DARE – Handicappers**

DARE to keep that journal we talked about at the beginning of this first F of FAILURE. DARE to take it with you to the doctor's office and your appointments. DARE to speak the truth of how your body is FAILING you. And here's a double DARE: if you can, allow your caregiver to accompany you into the doctor's examination room. Allow your caregiver to be part of your exams and conversations with your healthcare providers. DARE to allow this kind of intimacy, if you can. It has proven to be immensely helpful to me to allow my husband, daughters, and close friends to accompany me into various exam rooms (not all at the same time). They have provided support, humor, compassion, and even some important observations that alone, I could not have contributed. DARE to take your journal and your caregiver with you, into that small, lonely, bright room. DARE to FACE your FAILINGS together. It helps.

> *Most times I'm quite comfortable with my husband, a daughter or a friend accompanying me into the exam room. Sometimes, I'm not. A lot depends on the procedure and my position on the exam table. You get my drift? But most times, I have benefited greatly from the companionship of my dear ones and their more unbiased observations of my overall condition. I understand that this can be difficult at times, but I DARE you to allow your caregivers this opportunity. See how it goes.*

What do you think of this DARE?

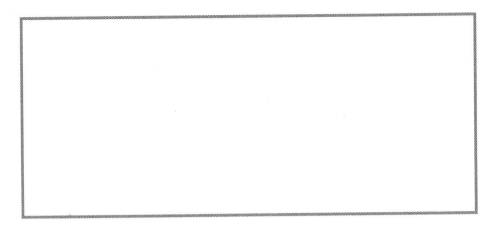

 DARE – Caregivers

DARE to hold your capper to the truth as you see it in them. DARE to let them know when you see improvements and when you see more FAILINGS in their bodies. The DARE I just laid on the cappers, I lay on you caregivers now: if your capper will allow you, and if you can handle it, accompany them into the doctor's exam room. I DARE you to be an active advocate, companion, observer, and communicator with both your capper and their healthcare providers. I DARE you to experience this level of intimacy with your capper. It is well worth it.

What do you think of this DARE?

Caregivers and Handicappers

I don't know about you, but I'm ready to say goodbye to this first F of Reaction to Disability, FAILURE, and move on to the second F of reaction: the fabulous, ever-present F of FRUSTRATION. Yahoo!

But before we continue on our roller coaster ride, let's pause for a moment ... We need to talk about something. In fact, we will talk about this "something" at the conclusion of each of the 5 Fs of Reaction to Disability in this book. The "something" that we'll examine at the end of each of the 5 Fs, is centered in the word ADAPT. As handicappers and caregivers, we may or may not be aware of all the various ways we are forced to ADAPT our previously "normal" lives. So, as I sit here typing away, on a rainy Thursday morning, I am prompted to keep this word and concept in the forefront of my mind and actions. Each F of Reaction we encounter demands that we, as handicappers and caregivers, ADAPT. So let's take a look at what it means to ADAPT.

> ADAPT – Definition: Make something (or someone) suitable for
> a new use or purpose; become adjusted to new conditions.

Whoa! Sound familiar to anyone? Become adjusted to new conditions? Are you looking for ways to become suitable for a new use or purpose in your life? As you read these words, please take time to reflect, think, pray, and write down ways in which you can ADAPT to the first F of Reaction to Disability, FAILURE. Ask yourself, how can I ADAPT to the natural experience of FAILURE in the FACE of physical handicaps? As I consider each of you who are reading these words, my heart is touched with love and hope. There are many good ways to ADAPT to physical FAILURES.

I encourage you to take time for review and reflection. Write below what it might look like for you to personally ADAPT to physical FAILURES, either in your own body or in the body of your capper. If you haven't begun to rank (0–10) and write about FAILURE yet, be sure to start now. Go back and read page 30 if you need help. If you have the *Facing It Journal*, use the preformatted area to rank and write about FAILURE. I think you are ready to reflect, think, pray, write, and ADAPT to what you have read about this F called FAILURE. Write in your journal, and write here too. You are beginning to take meaningful and purposeful actions. Good!

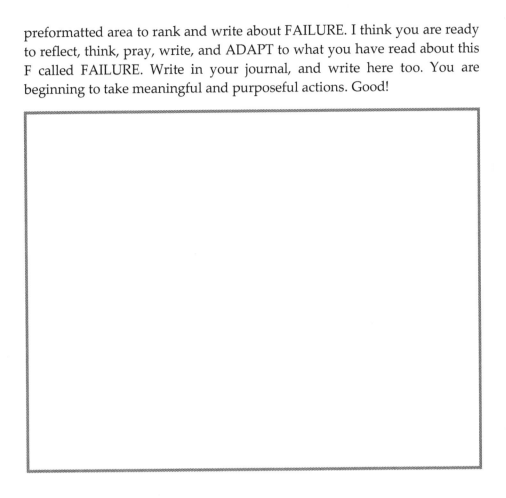

I trust you took the time to stop and reflect, and wrote down some ways you can begin to ADAPT to that first F of FAILURE, because now we're hopping back on the roller coaster of Reaction to Disability and heading for the tooth grinding, downward track of the second F — FRUSTRATION. Hold on tight.

Chapter 2

The 5 Fs of Reaction to Disability: FRUSTRATION

FRUSTRATION – Definition: The feeling of being upset or
annoyed, especially because of the inability to change or achieve
something.

Oh yeah. For me, FRUSTRATION follows right on the heels of FAILURE.
Note the apt definition of FRUSTRATION: feelings of being upset or
annoyed because of an inability to change or achieve something. The
second big drop on the roller coaster ride for me is this one. Due to the
unchangeable FAILURES in my body I can go downhill fast into
FRUSTRATION. I'm really getting irritated right now, just thinking about
writing about this one! Help! I hope you all know that as I write this book,
it is as much for my peace of mind as it is for yours. OK. All right, a deep
breath is necessary here. Okey dokey. I think I may be ready to take a
realistic look at FRUSTRATION in the life of a handicapper and that
capper's caregiver. But I have to be honest with you. This just plain feels
grim right now. But, I know I have to FACE IT and unfortunately, so do
you. This is a natural, normal reaction to the invasion of any physical
handicap. So, let's grit our teeth and get ready for the second F of Reaction
to Disability — FRUSTRATION.

DO – Handicappers

DO be prepared for times of uncontrollable FRUSTRATION. It's as simple as that. Be prepared to experience miserable moments, hours, days, weeks, months, or even years of FRUSTRATION over the FAILURES of your body. Sorry.

> *We have the two most beautiful, adorable, brilliant grandchildren in the known world. No bias here. As I write, Grace has just turned 3 years old and Lucien just turned 20 months old. It is our joy to have our daughters and their families all living within half an hour from our little house on the hill. We see these precious ones in our lives often and regularly. I know this is a huge blessing. Many parents and grandparents we know may see their precious ones only once or twice a year or less. Our family and our close relationships, one to another, bring great joy. But you know what? Ever since Grace's birth into this world, I have not been able to hold her close and walk with her. Ever since Lucien's birth into this world, I have not been able to hold him close and walk with him. I have not been able to lift them from their cribs, hold them to my heart, whisper words of love and prayer in their perfect little ears, and walk with them secure in my arms. I am physically unable. I am crying with FRUSTRATION even as I type these words. I can hardly see the keyboard. I want to lift, carry, console, play, walk, skip, dance, and run with our Gracie and Lucien. I can't. Pure, undiluted FRUSTRATION for this grandma. A FRUSTRATION to be dealt with every time they lift their outstretched arms up to their spazzy, one-eyed, handicapper Gammie.*

What gets to you?

DO – Caregivers

DO be prepared for outbursts of uncontrollable FRUSTRATION as your capper tries to come to grips with the realities of a FAILING body. DO be prepared to experience major FRUSTRATIONS yourself, as you deal with a FRUSTRATED handicapper. Good grief! What a load. What's getting to you?

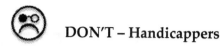 **DON'T – Handicappers**

DON'T be too hard on yourself when FRUSTRATION with your handicaps overwhelms you. But DON'T, and I mean DON'T, camp out too long on the downhill track of this F, or the Big D, DEPRESSION, will eat you alive.

Remember those two darling grandchildren I can't lift and carry or walk and hold hands with? They are coming up again. You see, their mamas and papas must drive them to our house, or someone must drive me to theirs. Because of my multiple handicaps, I shouldn't drive. Notice, I didn't say can't, but, shouldn't. Believe it or not, I do have a legitimate, legal driver's license, complete with a hideous photo ID. It's legal through the year 2010. If you want to see true horror register in someone's eyes, just look at my family when I mention that I really want to drive. I really, really want to drive — especially to see each of our daughters and Grace and Lucien.

I really want to drive to the store, the library, the zoo, the coffee shop, to church, and to friends. But, I know I shouldn't. Why? It's pretty apparent. I can't feel my legs or feet very well and they don't respond to my commands like they should. So, accelerating and braking at appropriate moments is beyond my control. And, with only one operational eye, I have zero depth perception, so passing other cars, changing lanes, taking curves and braking before impact would be risky business. I won't even mention parking. I hate not being able to drive. I hate it! This is a constant FRUSTRATION since I do have that all-important piece of plastic until 2010.

I will admit to times when I am tempted and no one but the old dog is around, to crawl out to our shiny, orange Honda Element and take a spin around the block. But I think it might just be exactly that — a spin. I DON'T stay too FRUSTRATED too long, because I know it does me no good and only harm. And I have no control over this part of my handicap. My body simply doesn't work right. At least, not right enough to drive safely. I also DON'T stay FRUSTRATED too long, because I know I am making the right choice. Besides, I love our orange Element, and would rather not damage its perfect body. It's the only perfect one that resides at this address.

Please take this DON'T to heart. Write about what FRUSTRATES you and how you can begin to live with these FRUSTRATIONS.

 DON'T – Caregivers

DON'T be surprised if your capper has a hard time pulling out of the downhill force of FRUSTRATION. But DON'T, and I mean DON'T, let them stay there too long. How long is too long? Sometimes, you may have to be the judge of that for them, and somehow with gentleness and, hopefully, humor, help them back on an upward track. Don't be surprised if they resist with even more FRUSTRATION. The downhill pull of this particular F is immense and can even pull you into that little car speeding down FRUSTRATION'S rails. FRUSTRATION with the one who is FRUSTRATED is quite common. I'm sorry. What are you thinking?

 DARE – Handicappers

So, here comes our DARE. DARE to pull out of the sheer downward force of FRUSTRATION. DARE to take a deep breath, pause and realize the danger of uncontrolled feelings of FAILURE and FRUSTRATION concerning your inability to do what used to be so easy and natural and normal to do. DARE to let your caregiver help you out of this awful place. DARE to take a deep breath, listen, calm down and maybe even laugh. Please.

I have to take lots of deep, calming breaths every day. I have to listen to my own good advice, the advice of others, and the perfectly, perfect advice from God's Word, every day. I have to laugh a lot every day. Often, I have to laugh at myself. Sometimes it isn't easy when I am FRUSTRATED with this body and the way it now malfunctions. I have to take my own DARE.

Probably the most frequent, nagging, constant, moment-by-moment FRUSTRATION I have to FACE is my lack of depth perception. I can't see straight! And sideways is a real pain. Don't get me wrong. I am grateful to see at all. My friend, blind from birth, and time spent in the waiting room at the Eye Clinic, have convinced me that I have it pretty easy. But ... I still get FRUSTRATED many times a day, as I misjudge distances in my daily household routines. I drop dishes, jam fingers in dresser drawers, pour coffee over the edge of the cup, stub my toes on the edge of the bed frame, bang hip bones into counter edges. The list of mishaps is as big as your imagination. Can you sense FRUSTRATION building in this Princess even as I write?

Oh. And then there's this writing. My one eye gets fatigued very quickly and I begin to make mistake after mistake in the writing of this book. There! In that last sentence alone, I made four mistakes that you can't see due to the wonders of this computer. Add two more in the previous sentence explaining I make mistakes. (It's probably time to quit soon for today.) A Princess certainly doesn't want to be clumsy, but this one surely is. Watch out if you are in close proximity to this body of mine. Often, as I go to hug someone, they'll end up with a poked eye or a scratched face. Fortunately, I keep my fingernails short, or there could be lawsuits. How extremely FRUSTRATING to hurt the one you want to hug! So many mishaps every day, all day long, I'd better take up the DARE to take a deep breath, listen, calm down and laugh. I'm willing to take up this DARE. Are you?

Name some ways you can take on this DARE. Be specific if you can.

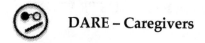 **DARE – Caregivers**

DARE to get close to your FRUSTRATED capper. This can be scary and maybe even dangerous, depending on how they act out their FRUSTRATION. You know them best. Figure out many different strategies for enabling them to escape this dark and sticky F. This is quite the DARE. On this one, I think I'd rather be the capper than the caregiver.

Please write down your thoughts on this DARE. What have you experienced so far?

DO – Handicappers

DO realize that working with health insurance companies, pharmacies, and physicians' offices can be extremely tiring and FRUSTRATING — sometimes bending patience to the breaking point. DO attempt to develop a one-on-one relationship with a competent individual in each of these venues.

> *It has helped me immensely to get to know over the phone: a good pharmacist, one helpful and caring insurance person who knows who I am and looks out for my claims, and the nurse or receptionist at my many doctors' offices. These are pleasant relationships and really help speed up what we all know can be hideously long delays on the phone. In my case, almost all of these one-on-one relationships are phone-relationships. Over time, we feel quite close even though we may never actually see each other. Some of these phone relationships span the country.*

Will you try out this DO? Where will you start?

81

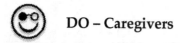 **DO – Caregivers**

The above DO also applies to you caregivers, if your capper is unable to do this on their own. I know from experience that it will help alleviate a lot of wasted time on hold and a lot of frustration when you know a particular individual to contact in each of the above-mentioned areas. And it is always nice to touch base with your phone buddies.

Do you need to take on this task for your capper? Are you willing to take the time to try this DO? How will you proceed?

 DON'T – Handicappers

DON'T allow the various health care systems to run you, if at all possible. When dealing with health insurance companies, pharmacies, physicians' offices, and even the health care pros themselves, DON'T let anyone push your stress buttons to the max. It isn't healthy! Laugh here, please. If jumping through all these health-care-hoops is too stressful for you, DON'T keep jumping through them on your own. Ask an advocate, friend, or relative to help you. Hopefully, someone with the patience and persistence of a bloodhound will make the phone calls and appointments for you. Such people exist. I know they do. As cappers, we DON'T need more stress in our lives. We need less.

Just yesterday, I spent at least 2 hours on the phone, yet again, trying to work out health insurance glitches and pharmacy coverage for my many meds. I was one FRUSTRATED Princess. My strategy for these types of calls is to try to pace around with phone in hand, while on hold. Can you hear me now? Clomp, drag. Clomp, drag. Clomp, drag ... I need to keep my step count up. But yesterday, I was pretty much tied to the kitchen table and unable to pace around, due to all the detailed paperwork I needed to weed through and decipher. Miraculously, I wasn't put on hold for half an eternity, but my bottom had to stay put in the chair as I dealt with a new health insurance company and prescription plan. I had to sit and sift through many papers as I was transferred back and forth via phone from California to Oregon over and over and over again. I talked to more insurance reps than I want to mention. I talked with doctors' offices and assistants. They talked. I talked. And eventually, I think (hope) we have come to some sort of agreement and plan.

But I can tell you, and so can my husband (poor man), that I was very FRUSTRATED with giving up those 2 hours. My eye was weakened from all the close up paperwork I'd pursued that morning, and as a result, I really couldn't read or write on the computer, because everything was just blurry. I was ticked. Even though I had accomplished what I'd reluctantly set out to do, I didn't appreciate the fact that it had taken 2 tough hours of close up eye-work. Believe it or not, this talker had really wanted to write yesterday! I knew what keys I wanted these fingers to punch, and I was ready. Wow. But, due to the long and detailed phone stuff, I was physically unable to fly with wings of joy to my computer and type. My one blue eye was done for the day. FRUSTRATION! And, I wasn't even able to clomp, drag, clomp, drag, clomp, drag, with phone in hand, to relieve some of the phone stress I always feel when pursuing these details. FRUSTRATION!

Always have a back-up plan. I did. I shot up my insulin, ate lunch, then lay down for an hour and shut my eyes. I got up and made my one good eye look long distance at one of my Leslie Sansone walking videos, and walked with Leslie one mile. It was the best I could do for the day. We had visitors coming over in the early evening, so writing was out; straightening the house and getting gorgeous was in. I was still FRUSTRATED, but better.

And today, I'm up early after a good night's sleep and typing away. Hi, you guys! So far, today is better. I am grateful that I am able to deal with

> *the phone details that are necessary to my health care. I am also grateful that I have, by experience, learned how to deal with the natural FRUSTRATIONS that come my way.*

What do you do? Do you have any back-up plans to deal with FRUSTRATIONS?

 DON'T – Caregivers

DON'T allow your capper to become overwhelmed with all the nitty-gritty details of their own health care. It takes patience, courage, quick thinking, problem solving, and math skills to navigate the waters of health insurance issues, prescription costs, office visits, etc. This might be too much for your capper to handle, in addition to their disabilities. This might be too much for *you* to handle. Get help if you need it. There are those who are willing and able to navigate for you both. Try to develop several strategies to handle your FRUSTRATION levels if you are the one dealing with the calls and paperwork. DON'T let yourself get slapped around with FRUSTRATION.

Any ideas? What do you think? How do you feel about these issues?

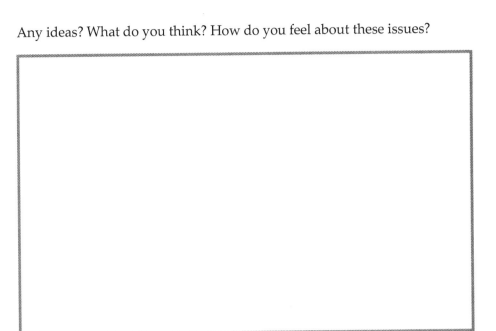

 DARE – Readers

DARE to take the time to seek out and establish meaningful relationships with individuals within each of the areas mentioned above. Initially, the time this takes can be daunting, but in the long run it is so well worth it. On many levels, FRUSTRATION will be lessened.

DO – Handicappers

DO know that when a person (you or I) feels helpless, FRUSTRATION is inevitable. Chances are that if you have to carry a handicap permit with you in the car, you are FACING the FRUSTRATION of helplessness, in some, or many circumstances. I hate it. This Princess wants control. This Princess wants to actively be in charge. Sometimes, I just can't be. Sometimes, this Princess is helpless. DO know this is FRUSTRATING. Being helpless doesn't help me or anybody else. Being helpless is no fun.

> *I am helpless in many situations. I don't like it. I must come to terms with my helplessness. I can't get out of this house on my own. I can't take my red walker on our gravel driveway and safely make it across the street to our mailbox. I can't pick up the mail or visit the young family right across the street, on my own. You already know I shouldn't drive. All these things and many more, prove to me that I am helpless in certain circumstances, because of my physical handicaps. FRUSTRATION!*

Are there situations in which you are helpless? How do you feel?

DO – Caregivers

DO know that feelings of helplessness will fuel big-time feelings of FRUSTRATION in your capper. Just be prepared as best you know. This is normal and natural, even if it isn't pretty and pleasant. DO help them feel less helpless. Only you will know how to begin to accomplish this. Think of some ways and write them down.

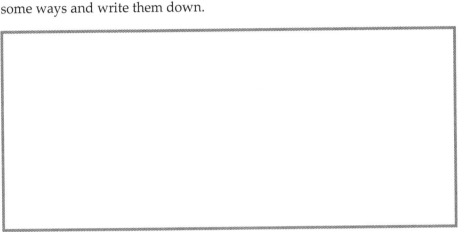

 ## DON'T – Handicappers

DON'T stuff your feelings of helplessness and resulting FRUSTRATION. Vent. Vent. Vent! — *Safely* and *sanely*, if possible. Think of some safe, sane ways to vent.

> *I vent a lot. Oh, I vent. Just ask the dog or my husband. My safe, sane ways almost always have something to do with noise. Big noise! I slam doors, throw pots and pans around, stamp my feet, and scream at the top of my lungs (into a pillow, or the neighbors would call the cops thinking the mad killer had attacked this handicapper grandma). If there is a way to make a big noise, I do it. Very simply, it helps. My husband understands, even if the dog can't.*

When FRUSTRATION strikes and you're feeling helpless, what are some ways for you to safely, sanely vent?

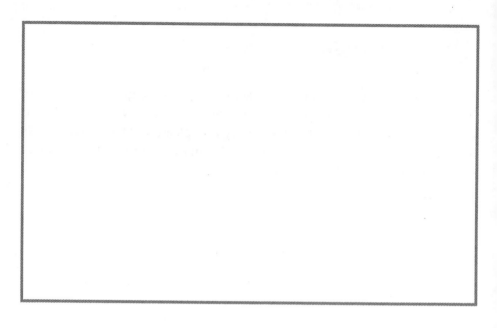

 DON'T – Caregivers

DON'T let your capper stuff their feelings of helplessness that will surely result in massive explosions of FRUSTRATION. They may or may not need help discovering safe, sane, ways to vent. Help them if they need some pointers. DON'T let them down on this one. And DON'T get in the way when they're venting. Venting is an absolute necessity when dealing with FRUSTRATION. I'm certain you will need your own venting techniques as well. Explore the possibilities!

What's your situation?

 DARE – Readers

Being helpless stinks. Having to watch someone you care for be helpless, stinks. DARE to take this stinky FRUSTRATION of helplessness and vent. Both of you will almost certainly have to vent. Accept this as a "fact of life." Happy venting!

DO – Handicappers

Just previously we were talking about a fact of life. There is something that must be addressed now: the "facts of life." Yep. You know where I'm going. If I were speaking this to you, I'd be hamming it up. Looking left and right, and over my shoulder, and spelling out the word S_E_X. (The birds and the bees are singin' and hummin'.) I don't know what your disability is, but my variety has definitely impacted the S_E_X life of our marriage. I DO need to be honest and open with you here, because many of you are in the same boat. We DO need to assess this important area of our lives and consider how we feel and how our mates feel. We DO need to communicate with each other in this rather delicate area of relationship, so we can be as close as possible in physical ways, without hurt or harm. Sometimes, this is a hard DO to FACE.

Type I diabetes has left me with very little spontaneity in my life. I used to love spontaneity. (Remember the otter in my personality?) My husband is an innovator in the sport of spontaneity. (He's an otter/golden retriever.) Jim is romantic, playful, funny, fun, sexy. And bummer of all time ... my blood sugar may be too low or too high to mess around. Or, I'm totally, physically worn out from a day of keeping this spazzy body upright. Or, I hurt all over from whatever it is that makes me hurt all over, so when I'm touched, even in the gentlest of ways, it hurts and irritates this body. My mind and heart are willing, but my body is not ... FRUSTRATION.

And you know it's not just FRUSTRATION for me, but also for my sweet husband. What to DO? That's for you to figure out on your own, with your own mate. I'm done with this "facts of life" S_E_X talk.

90

Is this an area you need to address? I'm not looking! Write. ...

[blank response box]

🙂 DO – Caregivers

Hopefully, you've already read through the "facts of life" talk I had with the cappers. DO know that there may be certain disabilities that will affect the way your capper can enjoy (I'm looking right and left again, and whispering) S_E_X. What to DO? You are on your own to figure out the specifics, but DO communicate in love and figure them out. I'm outta here!

[blank response box]

 **DARE – Readers**

This is one red-hot DARE. DARE to be honest and open with each other concerning this important issue of physical closeness and sex. This is vital. DARE to discuss and then DARE to DARE, safely, kindly, gently, and lovingly, with as much fun as possible. Go for it, all you cappers and mates. This is a good DARE.

DO – Handicappers

DO laugh on purpose. I've found that humor and laughter truly help to diffuse the constantly ticking time bomb of FRUSTRATION. I laugh easily. That works in my favor. I have a very funny family, and that works in my favor. Funny friends are always up to antics and that works in my favor too. This Princess is literally surrounded by fun and funny people full of humor. This is really helpful for my many FRUSTRATIONS. But, some of you cappers may not be easy laughers, or have a support group of clowns like I do. What to DO? Begin to find out what tickles your funny bones: books, cartoons, TV shows, movies, music. Seek out people who can get you giggling at them, at yourself, at the world at large. Somehow begin to learn to get outside of your handicaps and begin to laugh. Especially, when FRUSTRATION strikes like a rattlesnake. Laugh it up!

Our middle daughter took me shopping at our local health food store. She trusted me to hold on to the cart and manipulate the narrow isles by myself, as she shopped for herself in a different area of the store. I'm pretty good at maneuvering this spazzy body when I have a shopping cart to hold on to. However, they stack the produce tight and high at this little store and sometimes it's quite the challenge for me to safely acquire the items I know we need. On this trip, I had my eye on a lovely green cabbage.

The produce aisles were particularly crowded and I knew I couldn't safely reach up for a plastic bag and keep a good grip on my precious cabbage. (The roll of plastic bags was above the produce.) So, this one-eyed, easily dizzied, spastic shopper tapped the man just in front of me. He was standing with his back to me, right in front of the roll of baggies, which were beyond my reach, and he was tall. He half-turned to me and I sweetly asked him to please hand me a bag. He said "Sure," and rather clumsily reached out in the general direction of the roll of baggies. It was only then, that I realized I'd asked a blind man to help me grab a bag! He managed to get a grip on one for me and I reached for his hand to receive it, thanking him sincerely.

> *Only later, did our daughter let me know that she had observed the whole incident from a short distance away. Only then, did it get funny. She saw that this man's daughter was shopping with him as well. And when I dared to touch him and ask his help, she was about to swoop down and put me in my place. How could someone be so jaded as to ask a blind man for help with the roll of plastic bags? His daughter then noticed my apparent handicaps and revised her plan of action. I escaped the incident unscathed.*
>
> *When we were safely out of the store and our daughter told me this, I started to laugh with her. We laughed all the way home and continued to laugh as we told this story to family and friends — Gammie asked a blind man for help at the health food store and narrowly escaped the wrath of his daughter! My personal FRUSTRATION was turned into a humorous story. And that sweet blind man was, I'm sure, encouraged to be of help to someone else. I still smile whenever I enter that store. I'm smiling now as I recall the event. Funny stuff helps FRUSTRATION stuff.*

How can you load some funny stuff into each day?

 DO – Caregivers

DO find ways to help your capper laugh every day. "They" say that adults should laugh at least 50 times a day to be healthy. That is a high number to attain, so at least once a day, doesn't seem too much to try for. You, as caregivers, need these chuckles too. Just as was written above, DO find out what makes your capper laugh and you too.

94

What tickles your funny bone? How about your capper?

 DON'T – Readers

DON'T let a day pass by without laughing at something. Life gets way too grim and dark for us cappers and caregivers if we don't make sure to laugh, chuckle or smile at least once. Sometimes I've put myself in that grim and dark place on purpose, because I didn't **want** to laugh or chuckle or smile. I **wanted** to feel sorry for myself, and it worked. I DON'T recommend it.

> *I have indeed experienced days when I haven't allowed humor to invade my private, Princess pity party. These are miserable days, when I seem to assign myself misery. The bad thing is that my self-imposed misery invades all those close to me. How dumb! I know better, yet, once in a while I still let it happen. I say DON'T to myself, and DON'T to you too.*

How can we keep ourselves laughing in spite of the FRUSTRATION of the handicaps that we FACE? How? Write about this together, if possible.

 DARE – Readers

Laugh. Chuckle. Giggle. Smile. You need to, at least once a day; way more, if possible. This is a challenging DARE if you are one who doesn't laugh easily. Even if you are one who laughs easily, FACING FRUSTRATION with laughter and humor can be quite the challenge. I'm smiling at you, dear reader, right now. Will you smile back at me? Will you attempt to lift the heavy lid of FRUSTRATION and peer out at your current physical situation with a grin on your face and a smile in your heart? I DARE you to try. As we say to our grandchildren, "Show me your biggest smile!" Come on! I'm smiling at you — please smile back.

Will you accept this DARE to laugh and smile? Maybe you have a funny story you can write down right now, and laugh at together.

DO – Handicappers

DO try to find some way to serve other people, regardless of the handicaps FACING you. If at all possible, discover some way to help others. I think this will help you handle the natural FRUSTRATIONS that accompany physical handicaps. I know I am at my best, when I am able to help someone else. (I know it made the blind man in the market feel good to have helped me with that baggie!) This helping of others can be seemingly small acts of aid and assistance, but they are major boosts to those of us who daily FACE FRUSTRATION due to our own FAILING bodies. DO be on the lookout for ways to help other people.

I am pretty much a lost cause when it comes to being of any physical use to other people. I'm lucky to just keep from falling on old people and babies. But, I love to pray! I love to pray for people, with people, alone, or in a big group, with my eyes open or shut, silently or out loud. This is something I can do for others. In all my many years of praying, I have never had someone turn me down, whether they believed in God or not. Except once. It was a rebellious child and I prayed anyway. It proved to be the best thing possible, thanks to a loving God. No one else has ever said, "No."

God, Himself, in the Bible, promises to listen to and answer prayer. He wants us to talk to Him and listen to His answers back. What better way for this handicapper to help others?

How can you help other people?

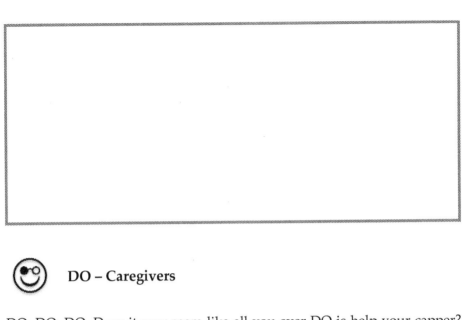

DO – Caregivers

DO. DO. DO. Does it ever seem like all you ever DO is help your capper? It's probably true, and a grateful thanks to you, from us. We need your help. But, as you read above, it is vitally important for us, as cappers, to be of some sort of help to others. Please stretch your DO list to include ways that you can help us help others. Please.

Can you think of some ways your capper can help others? Are they willing to try? How can you help your capper be of help to you or to someone else?

99

DON'T – Handicappers

DON'T ever think you are too handicapped or too disabled to be of help to someone else. Unless you are in a coma (I'm not joking here) you can definitely help someone, in some way. And, it will help you in ways you may have never even imagined. DON'T write yourself off as a victim of a crumbling body and wallow in the muck. DON'T fall for the lie. Help someone. Start today.

> As I have said previously, I am at risk of falling — falling on things, falling on people — falling. Period. But, I've found another way to help, as well as praying for others. At church, we have an infant room, where babies are lovingly cared for while their parents attend Bible study, support groups, service projects, church, etc. I am capable of sitting in a rocking chair. There are, of course, other able-bodied people on duty, so they do all the foot work, diaper changes, toy pick-up, etc. I get handed the sleepy, fussy, curious, cute, need-to-burp, babies. I hold, rock, burp and soothe these precious little ones. I even sing to them — softly. No one but a baby has ever truly enjoyed my singing. And they are too small to really object or talk back. So, cool. I'm able to help their parents get a break, and I am blessed in the helping as well. I hope the babies are helped too, in spite of my singing.

DON'T write yourself off as too disabled to be of service to someone else. Where are you concerning this DON'T?

100

 **DON'T – Caregivers**

DON'T write your capper off as unable to help you or others. DON'T let them write themselves off. Help them find ways to be of service to you and to others. Think with them, please. And help them to find ways to help others. DON'T give up on this DON'T. It's too important.

How can you help your capper begin this process of service to others? How can you help them maintain their service to others?

 DARE – Readers

DARE to find ways to help. Caregivers, this is an extra for you, and I know it. You are helping us cappers all the time. Will you DARE to extend your care a little bit further and help us help others? And cappers, will you DARE to seek out ways to be of assistance to your caregiver as well as someone else? Will you DARE?

Before you write below, I want to point out something very special — handicappers and their caregivers were the moving force that made "Handicap Access" a reality in this country. Our predecessors literally paved the way for us today. There are ramps where there used to be only stairs. There are elevators. There are special parking places for us permit-carrying cappers. Sidewalk curbs have been dipped out just for us. Because of previous handicappers and their concerned caregivers, things are better for the physically disabled and the ones that care for us.

Thank you, from the bottom of my heart, to those of you who worked so hard to make things easier for my caregivers and me. Thanks, love, and appreciation for your hard work on our behalf. You inspire me towards good works of helping others.

OK. Now let's DARE to think BIG, about how we can help other people. Any BIG ideas out there? Even little ones are good!

Caregivers and Handicappers

Before we move on to the next thrilling F of Reaction to Disability, FURY, I really want you to pause and think about the natural FRUSTRATIONS you feel as a result of the handicaps you FACE. What to DO about these FRUS-TRATIONS? How can you personally use the DOs, DON'Ts, and DAREs I've given you? How can you ADAPT them to your particular situation? Write about your various, continuous, clinging FRUSTRATIONS. Reflect. Think. Pray. Write. ADAPT.

How can you ADAPT to FRUSTRATION? Go ahead and begin to journal now concerning FRUSTRATION. Rank it from 0–10 and write about it daily. If you don't have a journal, it's really time to start one. Remember that the *Facing It Journal* is formatted to help you do this quickly. You can write here, too. Reflect and ADAPT to FRUSTRATION.

An Orange and Pink Interlude —
April 23, 2004

This evening Jim bought me a mirror! A beautiful round mirror, with shiny tiles of pink and orange encircling it! Why am I so excited? In the WHO AM I? section of this book, not only did I neglect to tell you that I hate roller coasters (that issue has been addressed), I neglected to tell you that I love mirrors! I've loved mirrors ever since I was a child. (It must be the Princess thing.) Anyway, in our little old house on the hill here, we used to have only two mirrors: one in the bathroom and one full-length mirror in our bedroom — two, plain, functional mirrors. That was it. Now we have three. And this new one is a wowser! Here's the story of my FACING IT mirror.

I had to have it. I'd walked away three times and returned three times to stare into it. I had to have it. It didn't make any sense to me, but I had to have the pretty, round, brightly tiled mirror that was hanging on display. (This was only the second time in my life that I was so drawn to a thing. The first time it was a simple but lovely ruby ring that I visited several times through the jewelry store window. We couldn't afford such a trinket with three little girls to raise, and I never even told my husband about this desire until weeks later. He was sweet enough to want to go and look at it with me, but when we got to the store window, it was gone. I had been very drawn to that ring of simple beauty. That was unusual. It stands out now as a clear memory, because things just don't matter much to me.) To be so strongly drawn to this shiny piece of glass was strange. Unlike the ring, I couldn't let this go. I had to have this mirror.

Jim and I were at Ikea, a fantasyland of Scandinavian home furnishings near Seattle, Washington. It is a huge warehouse of furniture showrooms, specific decorating items, foods — you name it — from the Scandinavian countries. You need a map to get around inside the place it's so big. I'm serious. They give you maps. I had a fun European-type cart to push around, so I was free to safely travel wherever I wanted.

We were there on a mission for our middle daughter. It was our pleasure. It is a long but beautiful drive to the Ikea store from Portland, and the huge store is just a blast to wander through. We were there to pick up a couple of previously ordered items of furniture for her new apartment. She had the money, but not the time, to make the trek to Ikea. We had the time, but not the money, so we offered to go for her. There we were. We had no thought in mind of shopping for ourselves. Money for us was very tight, and we were just having fun looking for her specific choices and gawking at all the rest of the things. Ikea is a colorful, well laid out extravaganza of Scandinavian stuff! It was fun to just walk around and look. So we were. Jim went one way; I went another.

As I wandered through many gorgeous living room set-ups, dining room set-ups, bedroom set-ups, etc., I landed in a little side room full of things one might place in a young girl's bedroom. And there it was — hanging on the wall. A mirror. The mirror. My mirror? That's what it felt like the first time I looked at it. Even before I looked into it, I wanted it. But when I looked into it, I was hooked. Like I said, I tried to walk away from this seemingly nonessential object, but I knew I had to have it. I simply had to have it. I didn't even look at the price. It didn't matter. I had to have it.

I tracked my husband down. He was headed towards the lamp section. I asked him to come with me to look at this mirror. On the way, I told him I had to have it. He looked at me the way he sometimes does when he thinks my blood sugar might be too low, and I'm about to go loco. But he went with me to this little corner of this huge store, and there it was, hanging on the wall. Even he thought it was pretty, but what did I mean by, I had to have it? It didn't go with anything else in our house, and we were very low on money.

I didn't know why, I just knew I had to have it — immediately. I needed to drive home to Portland with that pretty, round mirror safely placed in the back of our Honda, along with our middle daughter's stuff. I didn't even care what the price was. Whatever the cost, it was worth it. This was a must-have for me. Quite unusual! Jim took me at my word and got it for me. It was only $18.00! He packed up the Honda and we headed for home. I was very satisfied. Why?

 **My Reflection**

This mirror turned out to be a crucial buy — both an important and a helpful bit of beauty. Important, because of the date on which it was purchased. And helpful, because of where it was placed in our house. Later, in the book, I'll reveal the importance of the date on which we bought the mirror, April 23rd. (You'll just have to read on.) For now, I'll tell you why this mirror has proven helpful.

When we arrived home that night, I couldn't wait to grab my mirror and try it on various walls in our house. It didn't go well on any wall. Hmmmmm. I wanted to see the shiny pink and orange tiles and glass prominently on display. I wanted to look often at its beauty. Where to place it? Where could it go? Where do you think it landed?

Maybe you've guessed. It landed on my desk. Yep. On my desk, leaning on the blank white wall, just behind my computer screen. This is its home for now and has this piece of glass and tile ever helped me! I've told you that it's been hard for me to sit and write this book. Before we bought this mirror, my desk in the corner had little appeal. (I did like the pretty blue and green lights on the computer, when I closed the lid. That was it, however.) But placing this mirror just behind my computer screen brightened my corner. I began to look forward to sitting down and writing, with such a beautiful object right in front of me! This was helpful.

And — as the mirror sits FACING me, I have to FACE IT every day I write. Get it? I make it a point to look into this looking glass and think of all of you FACING IT as I sit down to write, FACING IT. Is that a kick or what? I take a good look at this one-eyed, supposed writer and have to laugh. I am FACING IT! And the mirror has made it fun.

God is so good. I know this FACING IT mirror is truly a God-given gift to this Princess. I am inspired to pray, think of you, and then write, every time I sit down at my desk and look into this mirror.

So much for the helpful part of the mirror experience; the importance of the date of purchase will come later — the conclusion to this orange and pink interlude. God is involved in this aspect as well. If you want to see this must have item of mine, you can look on the website, www.facingit.org, and see me FACING IT. It is a pretty mirror, and worth a look.

I think we're ready to leave FRUSTRATION, and move on to FURY.

Chapter 3

The 5 Fs of Reaction to Disability:
FURY

FURY – Definition: A surge of wild or violent anger.

Oh yeah. FURY. FURY! *FURY!* It is always close to the surface with me. I must tell you all, that as I sat down at the computer to begin this section, I worked hard for about one and a half hours, was drained out, and asked my dear husband to please print out what I had written. He sweetly complied. And then I heard him moan, "Uh oh. Oh no! It's all just been lost, deleted." I'd neglected to punch the "Save" key and all was lost. FURY at my own inadequacy did indeed surge up in a fit of wild anger. Duh! I stomped my spastic feet a few times, not angry with my husband, but with myself. Then, just as quickly as the FURY hit, it departed. What else do I have to do right now in my life? God has commissioned me to write. So, I will simply continue to write. Maybe the second time through will be better than the first deleted section. I hope so.

FURY is a common reaction for me. It always has been, even before my physical handicaps. I can flare up in anger quickly, express it loudly, and then, thankfully, forget it and move on. It's part of my personality. Repressed anger has never been a problem for me.

FURY is a reality for any handicapper and almost certainly for their caregivers, as well. It is a natural human reaction to FAILURE and FRUSTRATION. Just watch any toddler attempt and FAIL, attempt and FAIL, attempt and FAIL. You will probably witness first hand that FRUSTRATION leads to FURY. We all share that human reaction — from infancy to 110 years old. So, what are some DOs, DON'Ts and DAREs for us handicappers and caregivers when FURY rears its ugly head?

109

DO – Handicappers

DO know that we are going to experience FURY, big time, as people who physically cannot do all that we need or desire to do. Be ready for the powerful surges of FURY that will certainly occur. Remember in the definition for FURY it's "wild and violent" anger. In my opinion, this kind of anger is OK and probably necessary for us, but we need to be careful and set parameters for our outbursts. DO know that sometimes these surges of wild or violent anger will surprise us. We may suddenly be absolutely FURIOUS with ourselves, our caregivers, other people, or God Himself. Read on. This personal example of FURY is connected to an upcoming personal example of FEAR, but here we go anyway.

It was a perfectly lovely, early morning in Orlando, Florida. My husband and I were on a much-needed vacation — just the two of us. We'd flown from our beloved, cloudy, cold, rainy, Portland, Oregon, to the sun-kissed paradise of Florida in November. And now, we were waiting in line with tons of excited tourists, to be admitted to Epcot® at Walt Disney World®. Anticipation of a fun-filled day could be heard in voices, seen on faces, and palpably felt. It was great to be alive and be in this place. How soon would they let us all enter? I could hardly wait to start truckin' around Epcot with my red walker and my very own Prince Charming!

As we awaited the opening of the ticket gates, my Prince Charming, began turning into a toad. With a loving but serious look on his face, he told me that he was concerned about me. He didn't think I could physically make it all around Epcot on foot, using my trusty walker. He asked me to consider using a wheelchair. A wheelchair!? He'd be happy to push me around. Yeah. I was beginning to feel pushed around already. And we were still just standing and waiting in line to go in to the park.

Epcot is a very large theme park with a big, beautiful lake in the center. Basically, fun-seekers circle this lake and enjoy the opportunity to visit many different "countries". It is quite a hike. We'd been there years before, when I was normal. I thought I could make it just fine with my walker. As the wait to enter continued, and I stood leaning on my walker,

I could feel my legs already wanting to spaz out on me. I certainly didn't tell Mr. Charming, and I tried to deny to myself that it was happening. We waited. And waited some more. As we waited, Jim looked at the map of Epcot. He brought up the fact that in order to secure a park-provided wheelchair, we had to make the decision as soon as we entered the gates. The only place to deposit my walker and slap my bottom in a wheelchair was immediately to the left, as we entered the park. Great! I now know I'm in physical trouble just waiting to enter. What to do? Forge ahead in my typical strong-willed, often idiotic way? Or give in to my obvious physical handicaps? I really wanted to forge ahead. Deny. Overcome. But could I?

The gates opened and excited tourists began to pour into the park. Mr. Toad mentioned the wheelchair option, yet again. I was getting mad. "I can do this," was my grim pronouncement. He looked doubtful, and that just fueled my anger and determination. About 50 paces past the wheelchair option, he once more mentioned the size of the park and his concern for my ability to enjoy the day and see all we wanted to see. I knew he was right. This was our vacation. We were supposed to be having fun. He needed a break as much as I did.

Fine. I grudgingly agreed to turn around and go back 50 paces and turn in my dear walker for a stinking wheelchair! I was so FURIOUS with my FAILING body that I could hardly keep from screaming. Jim knew this was very difficult for me to accept and he did all the right things. (He truly is my Prince Charming.) But I remained FURIOUS, defiant, and humiliated by my lack of physical ability and stamina.

As soon as the pleasant attendant put an ID sticker on my red walker and wheeled it away to the holding area, I began to lose it. The smiling, courteous attendant assisted me into a pretty, blue, Disney wheelchair, not knowing that this Princess was about to blow up. As Jim began to push me away from the wheelchair area and into the park, I gave up and gave in to FURY.

I couldn't stop it. I begin to cry huge crocodile tears of outright FURY. Through tears and gritted teeth, I asked Jim to just stop the cursed thing and let me try to deal with the huge surges of wild and violent anger. We stopped. Through massive amounts of tears and sobs, I prayed. Remember now, crowds of happy adults and excited children were streaming past us — some with curious looks at a one-eyed woman in a wheelchair. Who, in *their right mind, would be crying just inside the fabulous entrance to Epcot?*

It took almost half an hour, but as I prayed, our gracious Lord calmed my FURY down, showed me my pride, helped me accept my true limitations, and prepared me for a fun day with my husband. I remember thinking, "Here we are at Epcot. I want Jim to enjoy this day and I want to, too. Help me, Lord, because I know I'll be mostly viewing children's faces and adults' butts." That thought brought a slight smile to my distressed face and I looked up at my wheelchair-pushing Prince and asked if we could just start this day over. He graciously agreed.

We had a great day. Jim was right. I would have never made it on my own two feet. I had FACED FURY head-on, and with my husband's help along with the help of my Lord, victory was gained. And so it was a perfectly wonderful day in the pearly, soft, sunshine of Epcot. I was taken by surprise by FURY. But I wasn't taken prisoner. Thank God.

Have you ever been surprised by FURY? DO answer this honestly. DO look for a glimmer of humor if possible.

DO – Caregivers

DO be prepared for frequent outbursts of absolute FURY from your capper. Help them know it is normal. Help them, if necessary, to find safe ways to express this wild and violent anger. This FURY must be allowed to escape so your capper can find some peace of mind and body and soul. DO know it is perfectly normal for you to experience FURY as well. Again, it seems, you have double-duty. Sorry. What can you DO?

 ## DON'T – Handicappers

DON'T stifle your FURY when it threatens to erupt. DON'T be afraid of this FURY. It is a natural outcome of physical disability. If possible, find appropriate places and times to let it all out. Find people willing to endure your necessary personal explosions. If you DON'T, you may end up like many, and like me.

Whenever I DON'T let off bursts of FURY, I end up with a splitting headache and a miserable attitude towards myself, others, and life in general. I know from first hand experience not to bottle up the FURY that lingers close to the surface of my disabilities. DON'T you end up with a headache and a bad attitude. Where are some safe places to let FURY roar? What are some good ways for you to let FURY fly? Write, you FURIOUS handicappers, write!

 DON'T – Caregivers

The same DON'T for your cappers, applies to you too. DON'T lock your FURY inside yourself. Let it out. Like your cappers, find safe places, people, and ways to release the FURY that has to accompany you, as our caregivers. How can you express anger in healthy ways?

 DARE – Readers

The DARE here is to *safely* let FURY rip! Cry, pound your pillows, slam some doors, stomp your feet, try the old "primal scream" and get it out. Both cappers and caregivers need this essential venting.

114

As part of my vast array of physical handicaps, there is one quite annoying and dangerous one. It is part of my rather confusing (to the doctors and me) neurological symptoms. It's called a "startle reflex." Over the past five years, I've learned to be on guard against this reflex, but I cannot overcome it. This is what happens. Any unexpected noise, whether loud or soft, can send my legs into tight spastic knots and jolt my body over backwards. (So, don't sneak up behind me and clap.)

I've mentioned our dog to you before. Now, I'll describe him more fully, especially in relation to this startle reflex. He is a beautiful, fawn and white, 11 year old Whippet. Whippets are sleek, slim, close-coated, dogs that look like a smaller version of the Greyhound. They aren't as mellow as a Greyhound. At least, our Whippet isn't. He thinks our house, our yard, our street, our neighborhood, and our hill belong to him exclusively, and he acts accordingly. He is an excellent watchdog. This means he will often startle me as I go about my typical handicapper day in the house.

Picture it, will you? A quiet domestic scene: I am peacefully propped against the counter in the kitchen, doing dishes. The Whippet is luxuriously stretched out on the living room sofa looking out the window for any possible reason to sound the alarm of intrusion into his territory. Spotting any type of "intruder", he blasts a series of barks to wake the dead. I startle. Begin to fall and then catch myself, hopefully, on the counter edge, before toppling over backwards. My heart is pounding — I just had a near death experience!

Right after my startle reflex is my FURY reflex. The Whippet knows what to expect. I holler at him, with a voice that could also wake the dead, "Cut that out! You almost killed me!" I scream it out immediately. He responds immediately, with doggy remorse and an apologetic wag. Of course, then I tell him he's okay, a good dog, and give him a love pat. This flare of FURY almost always accompanies my startle reflex, whether it is the Whippet that causes it, or some other source of sound. Unless I am in public, I usually yell, at whatever or whomever, to quell the immediate effects of FURY. Immediate apologies are often necessary and life goes on.

Will you DARE to let FURY rip? What can you do with this DARE? Both of you.

DO – Handicappers

DO be aware that a constant repression of FURY is not good. It can make you sick, and sicker. It can make you bitter, not better. Here's a tip. DO your journaling. Sometimes just writing out how doggone mad you are helps with FURY.

Write out your FURIES. Journaling has helped me handle what seems to be out of my control. Sometimes it seems my pen gets hot and the paper begins to steam. That's when I start to feel better. DO journal. DO write out your FURIES.

Go ahead write some FURIES down right here! Start to get them out.

 ## DO – Caregivers

DO help your capper to be expressive and even creative in their outbursts of FURY. Know this is necessary for them and let them know it is necessary for you.

How can you accomplish this? What are some of your FURIES? Go ahead and write them here.

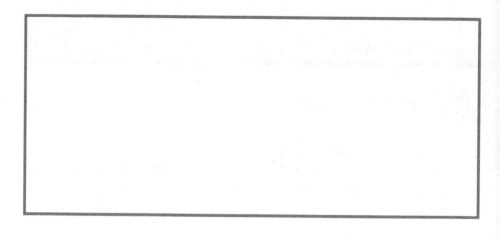

 DON'T – Readers

DON'T stuff that surge of FURY. DON'T pretend it doesn't exist and force a grim smile while grinding your teeth to powder. DON'T view FURY as some wacko weakness only "crazies" experience. DON'T allow someone to make you feel like an emotional FAILURE because you react to your physical FAILURES or your capper's FAILURES in a human way. DON'T.

Have you ever stuffed that surge of FURY? What happened?

DARE – Readers

The DARE here is to not let FURY use you. I DARE you to do your level best to use the natural reaction of FURY to physical disabilities, to your best advantage — both you cappers and you caregivers.

Get FURIOUSLY creative here! How can you use FURY to your best advantage?

Caregivers and Handicappers

Before we plunge ahead into the fourth F of Reaction to Disability, FEAR, I want you to pause and think about the expected and natural FURIES you feel as the result of being a capper or that capper's caregiver. What to DO about these FURIES? How can you ADAPT to the DOs, DON'Ts, and DAREs I've given you? Write about your individual FURIES. Reflect. Think. Pray. Write. ADAPT. (Right now, I'm saying, "Keep up the good work!" as I think of each one of you FACING your FURIES.)

Please write here how you can begin to ADAPT to FURY. If you have a *Facing It Journal* start to daily rank (0–10) and write in that journal concerning your natural reaction of FURY.

The next F on our roller coaster of Reactions to Physical Disabilities is FEAR. Oh, goody!

Chapter 4

The 5 Fs of Reaction to Disability:

FEAR

> FEAR – Definition: An unpleasant emotion caused by the belief that someone or something is dangerous, likely to cause pain, or a threat; often accompanied by anxiety and apprehension.

FEAR. Somehow all of the dictionary definitions of FEAR don't even come close to how personal and overwhelming true FEAR is. Look it up for yourself, and see if you agree with me. Just looking at the word can make me a bit anxious. Anyone who is physically handicapped enough to have to depend on other people for assistance in ordinary, every day life, has to know the very unpleasant reaction of FEAR.

FEAR surprised me. It snuck up on me when I was unaware. Remember, I grew up as the Princess, with tons of self-confidence, inner direction and outward support. When my handicaps struck, I was surrounded by the best of family, friends, and followers of Jesus of Nazareth. All my caregivers anticipated my needs and were sensitive to my well-being. I felt as safe as a capper with spastic legs, one good eye, and Type I diabetes could feel. We had lived in Portland, Oregon for almost 30 years. We had long-standing, strong friendships. We had attended Beaverton Christian Church for almost 14 years. We had brothers and sisters in the faith that I trusted with my very life. All our daughters lived close. A lot of extended family lived close as well, and all of these dear ones are excellent caregivers. So, what did I have to FEAR? What brought FEAR to the forefront of this capper's heart and mind?

Oh, I had off and on FEARS as I traveled the well-worn path of disability — all those scary tests the doctors thought necessary, especially the coffin-like, head-splitting, jackhammer MRI machine, that they kept shoving me into. But hey, I learned fairly early on that with enough Valium and headphones set to calming music, I didn't even have to FEAR the dreaded MRIs any more. I just spaced out.

Over time, I thought I had adjusted to the known pain of many common tests for neurological anomalies and I pretty much had. About 3 years into my disabilities, I was quite familiar with what routines occurred at which hospitals and with which doctors. I think it helped me a lot to know what to expect and to simply prepare myself for the physical, mental, emotional and spiritual stresses. I was very comfortable in my daily and weekly routines, since I had so many who knew what I needed physically and provided beautifully. I was seemingly secure despite my handicaps.

Then, the unexpected struck this Princess — overwhelming, uncontrollable FEAR. This was a huge surprise that completely humiliated me at the time. I'm still surprised by the FEARFUL reaction that overwhelmed this supposedly in-control woman. Here's what happened.

Two years before my handicaps hit me, the company he was working for treated my dear husband and me to a trip to Orlando, Florida. For nine blissful days, we stayed at a brand new, incredibly luxurious resort, completely at the company's expense. Wow! Nothing like this had ever happened to us before (or since). He had meetings for 5 of the days and I simply hung out at the pool, the deli, the room, and the shops. Back then, in 1997, this body was fully functional and I had a blast swimming, socializing, shopping, eating, and reading by the pool in my cute little 2-piece swimsuit. It was May in Florida and the days and nights were pleasantly warm — heaven on earth. During the evenings, we visited all the fun tourist spots. I had energy, stamina, enthusiasm, and fun with Jim. We had four full days to ourselves. This was the vacation of a lifetime. I can still relax just thinking about each wonderful day and night. Alright — this is just the preface to my upcoming FEAR episode.

Four years later, on September 11, 2001, we all know what tragic events occurred in our country. Even now, as I type this date, I feel disbelief and horror at the terrible destruction that occurred that day. Destruction devastating to individuals, families, businesses and all citizens of the

United States of America and citizens of other countries as well. Of course, as a nation, we were on high alert. Following the attacks all airports were trying to make secure whatever flights were in the air. Tickets were cheap, because very few people wanted to risk flying after seeing image after image of those planes plunging into the Twin Towers.

It was a weekday evening in October of 2001 when my husband proposed a fun idea to me, "Let's fly to Orlando again. Plane tickets and hotel rooms are so inexpensive, we can afford it." At first, I doubted we had enough money to do this, but he showed me the rates and we could. I was excited to think of vacation time in Orlando once again. Even though it would be on our tab this time, and I was now officially handicapped with spastic legs, a red walker, one functional eye, and Type I Diabetes.

That very same evening, as our middle daughter was reading on the couch and Jim was doing computer stuff in the living room, I was sitting in my rocking chair watching a bit of the evening news, while the possibility of another trip to Orlando rolled around in my brain. As I watched, the newscaster reported that some plane, somewhere in Texas, I think, had to have an emergency evacuation because of some perceived possible problem on the plane. The TV showed all the passengers and crew leaping out of the plane's exits onto those flexible ramps and sliding down onto the runway. My reaction to this scene was unexpected. As Jim worked quietly at his computer, and our daughter quietly read her book, I began chuckling. Chuckling! The chuckling gave way to soft laughter, which began to get their attention. As they looked over at me, I could see the question in their eyes, "What's so funny?" I began to laugh even harder as I got up and left the TV set and the living room to head into the kitchen to lean against the counter, laughing harder and harder. They followed me, looking a bit concerned and confused as to why I was laughing so uncontrollably. Then, to my absolute humiliation and dismay, I burst into tears. I was sobbing so hard I couldn't even talk. They had never seen me in such a condition, ever. I'd never been in such a condition, ever before. Amid hugs and words of comfort and humor, I started to calm down.

I began to recognize a classic case of hysteria. Hysteria? Me? Yep. When I could finally sit down and talk about what had happened to me, I saw that FEAR was at the core of my reaction. I had witnessed people forced to evacuate a plane by jumping onto that crazy ramp thing. And I can't jump. I really can't even bend my legs, hardly at all. In observing the frenzied exit off that plane, I knew that if I had been there, I couldn't have jumped onto the exit ramp and almost certainly would have gotten in the way of those who needed to escape. As I watched the news, I realized my helplessness in the face of such a crisis and saw I could actually cause harm to others because of my disabilities. I couldn't do what was necessary in an airline crisis such as this. FEAR absolutely slammed me.

I no longer wanted to fly to Orlando because of FEAR. As I talked this through with Jim and our daughter, I realized that I was way too comfortable in my every day routines and I depended way too much on all those watchful and loving caregivers. I needed to FACE this FEAR and put this dinged body on a plane and go with my husband to Orlando. It was necessary to stretch my comfort zone. Yikes! So, in November of 2001, we flew to Orlando and enjoyed a completely different vacation from the one in 1997. (You've already read about the wheelchair incident that took place during this vacation.)

After my surprising bout of hysteria I learned that I was so comfortable "zooming" in my grooves, surrounded by those who know me and my needs, that I had never FACED the FEAR lurking in my heart and mind. I had pushed it back and away and did not FACE IT head on. Jim was a great caregiver to offer a big diversion from my common routines and then encourage me when I melted down in the kitchen. Both he and our daughter urged me to go and experience my very first vacation as a handicapper. I complied. And I am so glad I did. I learned so much more about what it means to be handicapped without all of my normal, cushy support. So, what are some DOs, DON'Ts and DAREs concerning this frightful area of FEAR?

DO – Handicappers

As a handicapper, absolutely DO know that FEAR is going to be a certain, if not constant reaction to your inability to take care of yourself in some, many, or all physical circumstances. FEAR comes in all kinds of special and thrilling forms for each unique capper and our own thrilling, unique set of disabilities. As a handicapper, I DO know from experience, that we have to identify and acknowledge each one of our personal FEARS as we begin the long-term project of FACING our handicaps.

I don't like talking about my FEARS. I don't like FACING my FEARS. It scares me. It reminds me of my inadequacies. But, I DO know I have to identify and acknowledge each one of my personal FEARS, in order to begin to cancel their persistent pulling at my mind. As I begin to FACE each one of my "scaries," along with you, I realize that the root of all of my FEARS boils down to an acknowledgement of my lack of physical control. Even though I am the Princess, I am not the one in command of my physical circumstances. I want to be, but no dice. So, I can get very FEARFUL at times.

Do you want to talk about lack of physical control and the FEAR that follows? Neither do I, but I'm going to. In February 2003, I had the opportunity to go to the Mayo Clinic and Hospital in Scottsdale, Arizona. Since the hideous summer of 1999, my current neurologist had exhausted his search for the possible causes of my disabilities. He had hypotheses, but that was it. He is a well-known, excellent physician. He thought the last, best, hope for a diagnosis of something possibly weird and evasive, was to go to the Mayo Clinic and let a team of specialists go at me. Oh, boy.

Why not? Our insurance company agreed, and off Jim and I flew to the beautiful desert country of Scottsdale, AZ. It was cool, cloudy, and rainy the whole week we were there. We must have packed Portland in our bags. It didn't matter much to us, since most of the time we were inside the Mayo.

FEAR began to dog my heels even before we left our home. I knew I was in for constant, big-time tests and I knew that some of them would not be pleasant. When we checked into the Clinic and Hospital, it was kind of fun. The Mayo in Scottsdale seemed to me to be the Disneyland® of hospitals. There were friendly professionals everywhere, and lots of expert volunteers, ready to assist, to give directions, smiles, encouragement, wheelchairs, you name it. There was a lovely lobby, complete with a beautiful wall of fountains and a live musician playing a shiny, black piano — peaceful, soothing music, of course.

We met with the lead neurologist of the team of doctors assigned to me and I received my official patient itinerary. I was right. I was in for it. FEAR began lighting little sparks here and there as I anticipated all the upcoming interviews, exams, procedures and tests. FEAR of the results of all these invasions, sparked several FEAR fires as well. The roller coaster was fully engaged on the track of no return. I was stuck in the Mayo, in rainy Arizona. Help!

After tons of paperwork and two days of waiting room loitering, all the doctor "stuff" began. The worst was the spinal tap. The most fun was a cognitive skills test. Many other tests filled in the gap between these two extremes. After evaluating all the gathered info, my head neurologist and his team came to the same conclusion that my Portland neurologist had come to. They could see the obvious symptoms, but no obvious reason for them. No dependable prognosis. I could get worse. I could get better. I could stay the same.

But, there was one thing the head neurologist wanted to try. He wanted to see if I could safely get off a certain seizure medication I'd been on for 18 years. He thought this would help my long-term health and he was curious. He knew that the Mayo had a state of the art facility to see if this was possible. So, I was checked in to a new wing of the hospital, called the Epilepsy Monitoring Unit. The deal was to take me off my seizure med, cold turkey, and wait and see if I flew into a grand mal seizure. This testing would put me in a bed, plugged into a wall unit, with 30 electrodes attached to my scalp and face and chest for four days and nights running.

I submitted to the rather tedious, uncomfortable placement of the 30 electrodes. They let me look in a mirror — I looked like the bride of Frankenstein. Then they put me in a high tech bed, and plugged all my electrodes into a wall unit behind my bed that fed into the 24-hour video

126

and brain wave monitor. I was to be under constant human and video surveillance. It's a good thing I like to be the center of attention. All the special monitoring equipment and the person manning it were in the room next door. All this was for my own good, in case my brain flipped out and I went into a grand mal. Nurses would be called to my bedside, stat.

My FEAR factor multiplied exponentially as I tried to settle back in my special bed. The rails were up. I knew why. I didn't even have permission to move the rails on my own. They were afraid I might have a seizure, and hurt myself. They were afraid? Talk about FEAR! I was without the medication that had protected me for 18 years. I was under constant surveillance, so if I did have a seizure, not only would the person running the monitoring equipment see me, it would be on video tape, and many would see me out of control — total humiliation for a Princess.

The first day and night in the E.M.U. were the worst as far as FEAR. Jim stayed with me in the room. They had a chair/bed that he could sit and sleep on. What a dedicated caregiving man he was. The thing probably felt like a sarcophagus but he stuck with me for four days and nights. For the first few hours I was hooked into the wall and off my medication, I was franticly conversational. I was really FEARFUL, but not willing to FACE IT, so I talked. Jim listened and parried back the banter. After dinner, served in my railed bed, I began to get antsy and uncomfortable. The nurses were great. They gave me six pillows to push around my little space. I tried to relax.

It got dark and time to try to sleep. Sleep? I'm being watched by a stranger, off my seizure medication, and every seizure I've ever experienced, happened in my sleep! I didn't tell Jim, but I was getting very much afraid. He was on his pallet of a bed at the foot of my railed bed, softly snoring. He didn't know that I was so FEARFUL that silent tears were forming in my eyes and filling up my ears. All I could do was ask my Lord to please help me.

The phone rang. It was one of my oldest girlfriends. Jim was dozing as I told her the situation. She was so good to me. She comforted and encouraged me, and she gave me the tip that if I was going to have a seizure, what better place to do it than at the Mayo's E.M.U.? She was right. Thanks, Peg.

I was good for a while longer, and then FEAR attacked my mind again. I was aware of every heartbeat, every leg twitch, and every breath. I was *just waiting to go unconscious and thrash around on camera. I began to quietly cry and pray again. The phone rang again. This time it was another girlfriend in Portland, who just knew I needed prayer; and was she ever right on. She just launched into beautiful, heartfelt, needed prayer and I began to relax again. She prayed softly and sincerely and I knew the peace of God that passes all human understanding. Thanks, Stephanie.*

In fact, I sensed many friends and family, praying for me, and I just simply fell back into their support. Thanks, all. Then, I woke Jim and told him of my FEARS, that were now, calmed, and he read to me from the Bible until I fell into an amazingly sound sleep. The first night was down; I had three more days and nights to go.

The results of my four-day testing at the E.M.U. were uneventful. That was a good thing. I'd gone cold turkey, plugged into the E.M.U. wall for four days and nights, with no seizures. Yippee! Each day that passed, I got more confident. Finally, after four days and nights with no seismic events on the monitor, the doctors figured I was good to go — without any daily seizure meds.

Yippee again! I could get those 30 sticky, prickly electrodes off and away. And, I could at last take a shower. A much needed and much to be appreciated, shower. I was euphoric!

You want to hear about the shower? Yes? No? You're gonna' hear, whether you want to or not, because it was one of the funniest experiences of my life. And I *am* the Princess. So listen to this and laugh with me. Please. (There is a link here, to a previous personal story.)

Are you familiar with the famous Alfred Hitchcock thriller "Psycho?" (Yeah, I'm bringing up another Hitchcock film.) If you are, then you know the "shower scene" is famous for its absolute shock and horror. The images presented in that scene are vivid and memorable and make me want to only, ever, take a bath, and with no shower curtain, please. Maybe my "shower scene" will vie with Alfred's; only mine isn't scary, it's funny. OK. Picture this.

It'd been four days since I'd had a shower. (With assistance from the nurse, I'd been allowed to take a sponge bath and drag my electrode cords with me to the bathroom, near my prison of a bed, while camera and monitor were rolling. That was it.) So, when day four was over, all the electrodes were removed. My hair was full of leftover electrode glue, and my scalp was very itchy. I was ready for a real shower.

The nurse put the rails down and handed me off to Jim. I was extra wobbly and spaz-legged from being in bed for those four long days. You know how that is. So, I really needed his support as I prepared to enter shower heaven. Of course, I wanted to pull the curtain, sit on the ledge provided and soap up and shampoo, all by myself. No way. I was too shaky and unstable, experiencing the humiliation of this body's FAILURES, yet again. Jim was mindful of my desire for independence and tried as best he could to allow me some degree of privacy, but he had to hold on to me somewhere on my body at all times. I was at real risk of just slipping off the ledge on to the shower floor.

This wonderful shower experience was turning into an ordeal, demanding dependence and humility. It took a long time to safely shampoo, soap up, and rinse off. As we proceeded, I think Jim was getting as wet as I was, even though he was dressed for the day. It began to get funny ... very funny. We knew that even though the electrodes were gone, the video cam was still rolling and would be until we finally vacated this special E.M.U. room. Whoever was manning the video feed was getting an earful, if not an eyeful. Amidst a lot of stifled laughter, we had almost finished cleansing this Gammie's 50-plus body and I was physically fatigued by the effort.

The last spot to wash and rinse was the sweet "little" bottom that was precariously perched on the slippery shower shelf. Somehow, I had to stand up and let Jim do the washing. (I'm chuckling even now, as I type.) I gripped one of the shower safety bars with one hand and held onto Jim with the other. He helped me to a fairly stable standing position with my backend towards him. He's got guts! This was really funny, and even a little fun. Just as he was almost finished with this backend job, he dropped the soap. The slippery bar was now lying in wait, ready to slide under my numb, spazzy feet, and send me flying to the floor in a heap. What to do? Well, with one hand supporting my ample rear end, he had to lean way down and fish around the shower floor for the evasive bar of soap with his free hand. As he was in this rather compromising position, he looked up at me as I clung to the shower bar and with perfect comic timing, said, "Beverly just missed the opportunity of a lifetime." (Beverly is a girlfriend who had offered to come with me to the Mayo, if Jim couldn't get away from his business.)

> *The position he was in, and the position I was in, was just too much for me. I laughed so hard and so out of control that I lost it in the shower, like I lost it in the living room that day with my daughters and grandkids. (Thank heavens I was in the shower and not wearing jeans.) We laughed so hard and so long that our tummy muscles cramped in protest, but, oh, it felt so good to laugh so hard and so long. After all the shower excitement and surprises, I was literally a wet noodle. Jim soaped me up again. We had a final, uneventful rinse, whew, a wonderful towel dry, and he helped me into my own clothes. We dumped the hospital gown into the appropriate dumpster, Jim packed up all our stuff, and we buzzed the nurse. I truly needed the wheelchair she placed me in, but I was all smiles as I waved bye-bye to whoever was behind the video camera. Our stay at Mayo and the E.M.U. was over. The funniest shower of my life was over. We were heading home to Portland, family, and friends.*

To finish up this first DO, maybe you have a story about a time you FACED FEAR, and overcame it, at least for a while. Here's space to write about it. I encourage you to make it a good story; one you can have fun telling to others, and one that will remind you that you have overcome FEAR. If you haven't had that experience, then use this space to write thoroughly about one thing that you do FEAR, describing your thoughts, worries, and feelings about it — get it all out on paper.

 DO – Caregivers

DO be kindly observant of your capper. Notice what normal patterns of activity help them feel somewhat secure physically and what can make them nervous, anxious, FEARFUL or wildly hysterical. DO help them with your own unique set of FEAR diffusers: love, hugs, special signals, humor, challenges, dares, prayers ... whatever it takes to help them calm down and release that awful feeling of FEAR.

Please DO a similar writing exercise as I had your capper DO in the previous section from your point of view.

This is the first time in this interactive handbook that I give you two DOs in a row, followed by a DON'T and a DARE. There's a reason for this. FEAR is often unexpected and incapacitating. I know these DOs are difficult to FACE, but oh, so necessary. I encourage you to follow through with these DOs. I had to and it helped. I'm with you friends and hope is coming later in the 4 Fs of CHOICE.

 ## DO – Handicappers

DO look for the symptoms that FEAR is taking hold of your reactions to the circumstances you have to FACE as a handicapper in this world. I call these symptoms the *What Ifs*. These *What Ifs* build on one another. With each *What If*, your mind starts creating a worst-case scenario, and soon you're gripped by mind numbing, debilitating, all-too-real FEAR.

> *The morning we checked out of the Mayo Hospital, FEAR checked in with me again. I was released on my own, with no daily seizure medication, no nurses to buzz, no doctors on call, no constant video observation, and no bed rails. What if I had another seizure? What if it happened in public? What if I had one at the airport or on the airplane? My consulting neurologist at Mayo had given me a small supply of emergency pills to pop, if I felt like a seizure was "about to present." The same kind they used in the ER, he said. This was a possible, temporary fix. I clutched this little bottle, like Dumbo clutched his feather to fly. I was very FEARFUL and uncertain as to what my body had planned for me, now that I was without a constant wash of seizure meds flooding my "iffy" brain. What if I didn't recognize a seizure was about to happen? What if? What if? ...*
>
> *It's been 15 months now, since we left Mayo. No seizures in all that time. Thank God! I still carry my Dumbo pills with me at all times. I continue to need the "feather" close at hand. I still get the* What Ifs.

Every once in a while, FEAR prompts a *What If* to seize my heart or mind, or both. Some are ongoing, big *What Ifs* that must be dealt with over and over as they arise — *What Ifs* such as "what if Jim dies before I do?" Some are small, rather easy to handle, occasional *What Ifs* such as "what if I am speaking at some facility that requires me to climb a few steps to get to the microphone and this Princess falls headlong on her way to her beloved place of power — the microphone?" (That one's easy. Wear pants, not a skirt, and have an able-bodied assistant.)

Do the *What Ifs* ever happen to you? I'm certain they do. The best way to cope with them is to work out a Reply for each *What If* you think of. So go ahead and write down as many *What Ifs* as you can think of. Then, go ahead and write down Replies to your *What Ifs*. Example: What if I have another grand mal seizure? Reply: If I do, and boy, I hope I never do, my family and close friends know what to do. I've prepared them for this possibility, and they are armed with knowledge. The good news is, the longer I go without another seizure, the better the chances are that I won't experience another one. I hope so. This can be one of my nagging, on-going battles with the *What Ifs* of FEAR.

Do you get the idea? Please take some time and DO write down your own unique set of *What Ifs* and Replies. This will help you identify your FEARS and possible solutions. See what happens. ...

What If: **Reply:**

 **DO – Caregivers**

DO your own search for the *What Ifs* in your capper's life. DO communicate with your capper so that you can recognize those *What Ifs* well ahead of time and for as many situations as you can think of together. But once again, you have an extra assignment. You also need to DO a search so you can recognize your own *What Ifs*. Please write down your *What Ifs* as the caregiver, and your own Replies to these FEARS. Begin to sort out your FEARS and possible solutions. Write.

For Me

What If:	Reply:

For My Capper

What If:	Reply:

 DON'T – Handicappers

DON'T skip the above writing assignment. I know full well it is hard to FACE your FEARS and put them on paper. Hopefully, some solutions for diffusing your FEARS will surface, as you Reply to your own *What Ifs*. This is good. DON'T quit just because this is uncomfortable. Please FACE your own *What Ifs*. I'm with you in this one. Hang on.

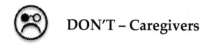

DON'T – Caregivers

DON'T ignore the previous writing assignment. Please read the DON'T I've written for your capper. This applies to you as well. Please write out your *What Ifs* and your Replies. It will help to get them down on paper. DON'T skip this opportunity to FACE what you have to FACE. Sorry. I sound like a drill sergeant rather than a Princess. But this *is* a bit like basic training.

DARE – Readers

The DARE here is simply to FACE the certain FEARS that will arise head on and with eyes wide open. (In my case, with eye wide open.) This isn't always foreseeable (get it?) and it isn't always easy to do. I have a very specific DARE for you now. You have just begun a list of *What Ifs* and Replies concerning your own unique set of FEARS. Hopefully, you are gaining insight into your FEARS and beginning to find some possible solutions.

Now, I DARE you to rank the FEARS you have identified. Begin with the worst FEAR you can imagine and wind down to the littlest FEAR. Don't worry. This is private stuff — between you and God. I can't see what you are writing. Maybe, at some point in time, you will be able to share your FEARS with each other, capper to caregiver, and caregiver to capper. Maybe you can DARE to share your FEARS with each other and arrive at a place of relaxation and peace of mind and heart, together. That's up to you.

I'll go first and give you just a taste of how I rank my set of FEARS:

> (1) *What If Jim dies before I do?*
>
> (2) *What If Jim is disabled in some way and can't continue to take care of me? I surely can't take good care of him.*
>
> (3) *What If I continue to get physically worse?*
>
> (4) *What If I lose eyesight in my "good" eye and end up totally blind?*
>
> (5) *What If my mind starts to go as haywire as my body?*

(6) *What If we can't pay all our medical expenses?*

(7) *What If I am alone at home and my blood sugar drops so low I go into a coma?*

(8) *What If I lose my voice?*

(9) *What If no one wants to hear me talk?*

Good heavens. I'd better stop there for now. I think you get the idea.

The DARE is on to rank your own FEARS in the box provided in this handbook. (If this is just too personal, write on a separate sheet of paper. But write!) This has helped me FACE my FEARS and I think it will help you, too. This Drill Sergeant Princess says, "Start ranking, now!"

Caregivers and Handicappers

It is once again time to reflect and ADAPT. Please review this section of DOs, DON'Ts, and DAREs, with an eye toward ADAPTING your lives and adjusting in healthy ways to your all too real FEARS. Before we hit the wall on our roller coaster ride of Reactions to Disability and FACE FINALITY, review this section on FEAR. Reflect. Think. Pray. Write. ADAPT. If you have a *Facing It Journal*, now is the time to begin to daily rank (0–10) and write in your journal concerning the natural reaction of FEAR. (I hope you are experiencing the benefits of meaningful and purposeful actions. This may be difficult, but it is very helpful as we FACE the FEARS of disability.)

Oh, boy. Here we go into the big curve … the vertical drop … the wall. We are heading into the fifth and final F of Reaction to Physical Disability: FINALITY. Just remember, we are strapped into this coaster car together. You are not alone. And neither am I.

Chapter 5

The 5 Fs of Reaction to Disability:
FINALITY

> FINALITY – Definition: The fact or impression of an irreversible ending; an action or event that ends something irreversibly.

FINALITY – What a definition. What a hard thing to consider. What a hopeless, gloomy, depressing expression of words that accurately applies to many of us handicappers and caregivers. The reaction to this FINAL and fifth F is a part of the roller coaster track I still cannot adequately brace myself for. For me, this is the second toughest of the 5 Fs of Reaction to Disability. (FURY ranks number 1 of the 5 in my daily life. Poor Jim.)

For some of us cappers and caregivers, FINALITY is inescapable: there's been an amputation, you've been blind from birth, discs in your back have been fused together, M.S. is a reality, permanent nerve damage has made you deaf, arthritis has bound your joints in permanent knots, you have Lou Gehrig's Disease, cancer has taken up residence in a previously healthy body, you've had a stroke, emphysema has you dragging around an oxygen tank … You name what it is that you are FACING, that places you on the irreversible downward track of FINALITY as a capper or a caregiver. Name what it is that forces you to take that handicap permit with you everywhere you go.

Go ahead and name it in the box on the next page. I know I had you do this before. But please do it again here. And know that my heart goes out to each and every one of you as you FACE FINALITY.

In my case, there simply hasn't been a final diagnosis of my neurological problems. Even after our stay at the Mayo Hospital in Scottsdale, AZ., in February of 2003, all that the doctors (and there were plenty) could track, were the obvious symptoms of some sort of "neurological event" that adversely affected my body, in the summer of 1999. When I was released from Mayo, my main neurologist, smiled, shook my hand and said, "I wish we had some definitive news for you. But all we can say is that we do not know what occurred in your body to display such obvious neurological symptoms." Prognosis — he said I could get worse. (Oh no!) I could get better. (Oh yes!) I could remain the same forever. (Well, that's interesting.) How am I to deal with this stinking fifth F of FINALITY? Neurologically, we don't know anything for sure. So, at the present moment, I am still a spaz with only one good eye, no depth perception, and Type I diabetes. What does my future hold? I don't know. This has made FINALITY a tough call for me, my family, and my friends. I am OK with it, mostly. (It is definitely better than a sure diagnosis of MS, or Lupus, or cancer, etc. — some of the things some of you other cappers and caregivers have to FACE.) Neurologically, my FINALITY is somewhat open-ended.

However, I do have to FACE the FINALITY of irreversible nerve damage to my right eye, and a certain and irreversible diagnosis of Type I diabetes that slammed my body during whatever happened in the summer of 1999. I literally have to FACE this one-eyed FACE of mine in the bathroom mirror every morning as I brush my teeth, and in my FACING IT MIRROR as I type. Oh baby, that's FINALITY! (We can smile here, if we want. I want. Thanks.)

For those of us with Type I diabetes there is true FINALITY accompanied by the necessity of physical, mental, emotional, and spiritual ADAPTATION. Food, timing of meals, exercise, medications, blood sugar checks (ouch), insulin injections (ouch again), can become all-consuming. It takes many people many years to ADAPT to a healthy diabetic lifestyle, and some never are willing to do so. The FINALITY of this disease is devastating to some, and challenging to others. I understand. I view my diabetes as one of my handicaps that I can control to some degree, depending on my willingness to pursue a healthy diabetic lifestyle. I try very hard to be in control of this aspect of my life, because I *can*. The rest of my physical stuff is beyond my active control. So, I think you can see why some days I feel the full force of the downward pull of FINALITY, and some days, I feel the upward surge of hope, of at least partially reversing some of the physical symptoms so evident in this very human body. Talk about a roller coaster ride.

But, that's just my ride. What is yours? So many cappers and caregivers must FACE, square on, the fact of physical FINALITY. The natural human reaction to this 5th F is awful. To have to FACE an irreversible physical handicap is naturally overwhelming, challenging, confusing, and depressing — for both the capper and the caregiver. So many adjustments must take place. And "WHY?" can rear its ugly head and butt heads with us often. The "WHYS" can leave us dazed and hurting and feeling very bruised.

Well, here we go with the 5th F of FINALITY, as we FACE the DOs, DON'Ts and DAREs staring us in the FACE. Let's get a good grip on that safety bar pressing into our laps. The roller coaster is headed full throttle towards the irreversible FINAL dive. We are stuck on the track, blazing towards FINALITY. Scream if you want; it might help. I'm a screamer. I'll scream right now, sitting at the keyboard. There. At least one of us has screamed. But as I force my eyes open, against the g-force of this FINAL twisty-turn, I see FINALITY looming as a huge, gray, uncaring, immovable wall. Graffiti is scrawled all over it: grief, loss, pain, "WHY?" This ride is no fun. Let's just lean into the comfort of one another as we ride into this 5th F. We need each other for this one. I'm starting to scream again. Will you hold me tight? I need you and you need me. We're in this FINAL turn together. The wall is too big for just one alone. Thanks for being with me.

DO – Handicappers

DO know that this 5th F of FINALITY concerning any physical disability is tough to FACE. Period. But FACE IT we must. My natural human reaction to the physical facts of certain, FINAL, disability, is to want to run away, deny, give up, ask WHY, quit, cry my eye out, go to sleep and stay in bed forever. Remember, I'm the Princess, and I'm so used to having my way made smooth and easy. FINALITY and the outright reality of my disabilities challenge who I am and how I am in this world.

> *It's been 5 years since physical handicaps slammed me to the floor the way Godzilla slammed our Irena to the floor in her black belt contest. If you remember, she popped back up and won her contest. I can't pop back up. Oh, trust me, I want to, but I'm physically unable. If I want to get back up off the floor, I need someone to help me. I hate it! But that is the reality of FINALITY in my life. I need help to walk, to see, to recover quickly from low blood sugar. I need help. What do I need? I need help. FINAL answer? What else do I need? I need to ADAPT. FINAL answer? (Isn't this grim stuff? Don't worry; there is good news coming.)*

It's time for you, capper, to FACE the grim task of writing about what won't ever change for you. Or what is unlikely to change. DO face FINALITY by writing about it. What does FINALITY feel like to you?

 DO – Caregivers

DO know that this 5th F of FINALITY will have you almost as fully engaged in all of the physical, mental, emotional and spiritual reactions as your capper. After all, you care. You are an observant and active participant in the trials of your capper. Your life must change and ADAPT as ours does. Your natural human reactions may be like your capper's. You want to quit, stop, rest, deny, go away, ask "WHY?" over and over, cry your eyes out, and just sleep and dream of better days. Our physical disabilities may very well challenge who you are, and how you are in this world. How do you feel about the FINALITY in your life as you care for your capper? It's your turn to write. Please DO.

DON'T – Handicappers

DON'T ever, ever, ever totally give in or give up. Always hope. Now, I know that there are times of absolute FAILURE, FRUSTRATION, FURY, and FEAR that can lead to a deadly sense of FINALITY. I've been there. But I also know, I'm still here — handicaps and all. I haven't hit the FINAL FINALITY of all. I'm not dead, yet! So, there must be a reason for me to still be around. Hope. Hope for a further recovery. Hope for a cure for diabetes. (Wow would that be something!) Hope that my blood sugar will allow me half a brownie after supper tonight. Hope that my life could encourage others in some way. Hope that Jim will take me to breakfast Saturday morning. Hope to see my grandkids, and nieces and nephews grow up. Hope to give hope to some who are hopeless. There are so many reasons for hope — large hopes and smaller hopes. DON'T ever, ever, ever, totally give in or give up. Hope. Hope. Hope.

What are some things you can hope for?

DON'T – Caregivers

DON'T you, as caregivers, ever, ever, ever totally give in or give up either. Please read the previous DON'T for your capper. And follow suit. Please write out some of your hopes.

DO – Readers

While we're at it, let's add thankfulness to hope. This really helps me when I come close to slamming into that hideous wall of FINALITY. Maybe this will help you too. What are some things I'm thankful for? My Lord. The Bible. My husband. My family. Friends. Pets. Our home. The beautiful Oregon coast. Sunrises and sunsets. I can wear short hair. I can still see out of one eye. We live in a free democracy. I'm thankful jeans are acceptable attire even for grandmas. I'm also thankful for my red walker. For messages left on our phone from dear ones. For in-house bathrooms with flush toilets. For notes and cards and gifts from friends and family. I'm thankful that people still seem to want to listen to me talk. And of course, I am thankful for you, dear reader. I could once again, go on forever.

How about you? Will you write down some things you are thankful for? Maybe this is hard for you. DO this together, capper and caregiver, if at all possible. DO try to think of at least one thing you can be thankful for. I have found that thankfulness is essential to ADAPTING to FINALITY.

Please help yourself and write. What are you thankful for?

 **DARE – Readers**

The DARE here is probably a lifelong DARE, depending on the handicaps we FACE together. The DARE is to overcome, endure, accept, enjoy life to the fullest, be hopeful, be thankful, and ADAPT, no matter what. This is the biggest DARE of all, so far, especially since FINALITY seems such a downward track. I know I am unable to fight the effects of the downward g-force of FINALITY without help. I know I must constantly ADAPT to this 5th F of FINALITY and keep on ADAPTING. I know this from personal experience on the coaster. Keep on keeping on. I encourage you. Will you keep on encouraging me? Let's DARE to say "Yes," to hope. "Yes!" Let's DARE to say "Yes," to thankfulness. "Yes!" And, "Yes!"

Here's one last box to write about FACING FINALITY head on. Who can help you do it? What other resources do you have? Is there a book that will lift your spirits? Or music? Or a poem? Is there an activity that you can DO that gives you the courage to ADAPT to the FINALITY of your situation? Write here.

DO - Handicappers

I don't know how long you have been FACING your physical handicaps, but I have a question for you. Something really weird happened to me just recently, and I realize it has to do with the FINALITY of my physical situation. I simply can't see myself ever walking freely down our hill, by myself. That's weird. In the first few years of disability, I used to be able to at least visualize this Princess striding with rhythm, balance, and grace, down the hill to my friend's house. But I can't anymore. I guess the years of disability have not only affected my body, but my brain. I can't even imagine myself now, walking without help. I've tried. I've really tried. I can't. I'm curious. Has something like this happened to you? Have you experienced this same kind of phenomenon as you FACE your own FINALITIES? How does it make you feel? Please write about it.

What to DO about this creeping, all out invasion of FINALITY — an invasion that not only occupies our bodies, but our minds? (This is beginning to sound like one of the scariest black and white movies of all time: *The Invasion of the Body Snatchers*.) I'll tell you what I DO. I consciously take time to try hard to remember the things I used to be able to DO. And I really enjoy remembering the DOING. I remember holding each of my baby girls close in the middle of the night and walking them around the house patting their backs for a burp. I remember the feel of

150

their small hands in mine as we walked to the grocery store. I remember wrestling matches with our girls on our bed. I remember dancing with them in my arms. I remember slow dancing with my Jim. I remember vacations, hiking, swimming, training the dog. I remember mowing, weeding, planting, hanging fresh, clean clothes on the line, when our Oregon sun made an appearance. I remember driving where I wanted, when I wanted. I remember seeing clearly with both eyes all the beauty of family, friends, and almost all of our 50 states plus many famous national parks and monuments. I remember looking at my face in the mirror as this Princess deftly applied eye makeup to **two** seeing eyes. I remember riding my bike, roller skating, playing hopscotch, and jumping rope for hours on end. I remember playing racquetball, tennis, ping-pong, volleyball, basketball. I remember eating all the chocolate chip cookies I wanted, enjoying a huge bowl of popcorn with a movie at home, slurping giant milkshakes in the car as we drove through desert country, without the danger of blowing the lid off of my blood sugar monitor. Freedom! Absolute freedom of body!

When I DO this remembering, it helps. The memory of fun activities cheers me up. At different points in my life, these were every day occurrences. This is amazing to me now. They are physical impossibilities for me now. But memory-tripping has helped me settle with FINALITY. Maybe it will help you too. Will you try? Throw yourself into fun, physical activities you once enjoyed. Enjoy them now in your memory. DO try to involve all 5 of your senses as you remember: sight … sound … touch … smell … taste. Have fun. Here's a personal example of enjoying all 5 senses in a memory.

I used to love to climb the steps up to a diving board, walk the plank to the edge and look down into deep water. I loved the thrill of attempting a perfect dive and the feel of my body flying through the air and slicing into the water. No more. This is now a physical impossibility for me. Big bummer! But I can remember using arms and legs to climb the steps; the rough feel of the steps and the board; the feeling of freedom as I walked the length of the board; bright sunshine; warm air on wet skin and hair. I remember the smell of the water and sunscreen; the sounds of others in the pool; the great sensation of hitting the water well and the pain of hitting it poorly. I can hear the sound of entering the water and then surfacing. I can taste the water. I can experience the pure joy of swimming and the sting of chlorine in my eyes. I smoothly move my body through the water to the steps up to the deck. And then go again and again. I loved the

> *challenge of always trying to improve my entry into that inviting pool of*
> H_2O*.*
>
> *Just sitting here at this computer, remembering how great it was to be*
> *able to climb a ladder to a diving board and then dive off into the deep pool*
> *of water, relaxes me.*

DO try this for yourself. See how you feel. Write some good memories now. Does this activity help you settle with FINALITY like it helps me?

As a handicapper, maybe there has been no time in your entire life that you have been free of your disabilities. I know there are many of you out there. Maybe you can try this: DO your level best to imagine what it would be like to DO some of the things you've never been able to DO. Try to engage your mind in some fun activity that your body would enjoy, if it could comply. DO try to engage all five of your senses in this imagining: sight, sound, touch, smell, taste. (I'm not in this category of cappers, but there are some activities I have never attempted and now, it is impossible for me to even try. So, I'll imagine something with you.)

I've never skydived. But I can sure imagine how it might be. I imagine the sound of the plane and my racing heartbeat; the sight of the ground so far below and the fluffy clouds I'll be falling through. I can almost smell the plane engine mixed with the smell of anticipation and fear clinging to my body. The feel of the (hopefully) trusty parachute strapped to me. The sound of the door opening, knowing that someone is going to have to shove me out of it. The palpable taste of fear and challenge; my hands triple checking to make sure I know where that all-important cord is I'll have to tug as I plummet to the earth. Cold wind rushing with a mighty force as I jump ... the fall ... the tug on the cord ... and the wait for the catch of the chute. I imagine all the sights, smells, sounds, tastes and the incredible sensations as I free-fall; until it all ends in the abrupt landing. Hope I don't break anything. Whew. I'm safely down. Let's go again!

See if this imagination-tripping helps you deal with the FINALITY of your own set of handicaps. I hope it helps you like it helps me. DO try. Write of something you've never been able to DO. Experience it as much as possible in your imagination. Have fun all you cappers.

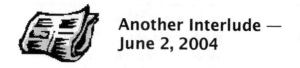

Another Interlude —
June 2, 2004

Early this morning, Princess Pam clipped the graffiti covered wall of FINALITY with an out of control roller coaster car. The car is dented but still on the track. The wall wasn't damaged at all. The Princess suffered minor injuries and is now on the mend ... details to follow.

At times I know I can sound like a Pollyanna. But I'm not. The reality of my handicaps keeps this Pollyanna-possibility under control. And today, the reality of FINALITY took out any Pollyanna potential lurking in my Princess mentality.

I hit the wall early this a.m., while Jim was off at work. It's now 2:45 p.m. and I really want to tell you what happened. But my eye is so worn out from crying, that it's too hard to continue trying to focus on this screen and type. So, I'll be back as soon as my eye recovers, with the rest of the story.

JUNE 4, 2004

I'm back. It took a good 2 days for me to recover enough to sit down in this chair and FACE my mirror and you and the jarring slam of FINALITY that incapacitated me since last I wrote. Well, so much for this fabulous writer and talker of FACING IT. Being a physically handicapped human being is hard. I'm living proof of that. I won't even ask you if you want to hear what happened. You know I'm gonna tell you, whether you answer yes or no. Here's what happened to me. See if you can relate. I'm trying to see your faces as I look straight into my shiny mirror right now.

I think the easiest thing to do, is to just type here what I scribbled (with tears flying) in my *Facing It Journal* for June 4, 2004. I wrote over the whole journal page in desperation. That happens sometimes.

"I'm hitting the wall. That hideous wall of FINALITY I've been writing about. Hit early this a.m. Pain. Grief. Loss. Very physically down (or up, I should say) because of high blood sugar. Number is almost 400. Feel dizzy, sick, etc. Already had 3 shots of insulin to try and make up for the ½ a

154

dessert shared with a friend last night after a light dinner out. Blood sugar still way too high. Angry. Frustrated. Can't I even enjoy ½ a dessert with my friend, without paying big time? Know exercise would help, but I can't when my sugar is so high. It's dangerous to move much when sugar is so high. Great. Crying. Can't believe I really want to write, but again, with blood sugar so high, my brain won't engage well. Can't write. So, what to do? Cry some more. Feel rotten and useless. Jim's gone, so I can really wail away at my pathetic situation. Once again, I'm stuck in the house on a perfectly, gorgeous Portland spring morning. I can't even make it out to the front porch to water our flowerpots. Physically shot. And shot up with insulin that obviously isn't countering my high b.s. levels. Sobbing now, at FINALITY'S grim, steady, stare down. FINALITY is winning at this moment. I'm giving in for now. So here I go.

———— I MISS — freedom of motion, exercise, watering my flowers, mowing, walking our hilly neighborhood, driving, shopping on my own, hanging clothes on the clothes line, chopping wood for the wood stove, food freedom, spontaneity. Boo hoo. As long as I feel this miserable, I'm going way back to things I MISS that aren't even related to this handicapped body. These are FINAL losses too. Let it rip. I MISS — being a young wife. Mama to three little girls. The constant activity that surrounded me. Baking bread. Making yogurt. Nursing babies. Fixing owies and kissing hurts away … being intensely needed. I feel absolutely useless and unneeded at this moment. And I am. Useless. Unneeded. A pitiful, teary, mess of a woman, just penning my sorry way into my journal. More tears. (Jim will know something's wrong when he gets home and sees my face and puffy eye. Oh well.)   I am so very tired of quiet. It's too quiet here. Being home alone so much. Being dependent. Dependent. Dependent. I feel so isolated and helpless. I don't just feel this way … it's true. Cry some more. Boo hoo. The old dog comes over and gives me a lick. I need it. Thanks buddy.

Beginning to recover some emotional control. Some. I feel battered all over and kind of sick. Like I felt after riding the 'Revolution' ride at Magic Mountain."

That dip in the roller coaster track was a big surprise. (Doesn't it seem like I get surprised a lot?) I really wasn't ready for the sudden drop and twist in the track that had me clipping the edge of the wall of FINALITY. I'm sure glad you were there with me in the car. You were, you know. As I was wallowing in my own personal well of misery, I thought of you tearfully grasping for a hand-hold on that tight metal bar that keeps us both from flying out of the car as we dip and turn on the track of Reaction to FINALITY. Thinking about you, helped me recover from my in-your-FACE encounter with that mud-ugly wall. Thanks for riding with me, Brave One. I need you by my side. Hope you weren't wearing your best shirt because I know I soaked your shoulder with my tears.

After this awful experience I asked myself some questions. What did I learn? What can I teach? OK. What did I learn? I learned I can still be surprised by FINALITY in its roughest form. Still — probably for always. I learned to ask for help. And I did ask for help. I prayed and God provided. Out of the blue, all three daughters called that day and listened to this Gammie cry. They were excellent over-the-phone caregivers. Jim came home and saw my sorry state. He, too, took good care of me. God knew I needed Him and them, and He provided beautifully in my ugliest of times. I learned to ask for help when I was helpless on my own to FACE the wall.

What can I teach? Write. Write. Write. I want you to learn to write in your journals. I cannot express to you how much it helped me to scribble down my darkest feelings. Writing, at the moment, helped me FACE the awful downward drag of FINALITY. It helped me get the sick, helpless, useless poison out of my system. Scrawling along through my tears helped me think about you. I want to help teach you to write, write, and write some more in your journals as you FACE your handicaps. (And I'm the talker!) In the writing of this book, I have come to recognize my daily journaling as an all-important indicator of my every day well being. Journaling helps me recover from sudden surprises on the track and helps me see potential dips and curves **before** I encounter them. I realized I hadn't written in my *Facing It Journal* for a week. No wonder FINALITY surprised me! Write in your journal, Dear Companion, it's indispensable. Write. Keep writing. Every day.

And think about this. As you work your way through this interactive handbook for handicappers and caregivers, you are (hopefully) writing your way along with me. You are already practicing writing. Whenever you decide to journal, your personal situation will improve because you will become an active, informed participant in FACING the disabilities that

156

must be dealt with daily. That is a helpful and good thing. So, once again, I urge you (urgently) to journal. I'm talking to myself here too. I know I can't afford to skip many days or I could be surprised again, and that is one surprise I'd rather do without.

I don't think it was an accident of fate that I hit the wall of FINALITY just after writing to you about good memories, hopes and thankfulness. (As I look back on the incident now, I can see it was a good thing to slam into the wall of FINALITY after writing down all the good stuff I could think of.) I needed to once again experience the awfulness of FINALTY and scribble my miserable notes. You know why? So that as I recovered, I could turn back the pages of this book and review all the good stuff: the DOs, DON'Ts and DAREs of FINALITY. How good it was to look at my sweet memories, hopes, and all the things I am thankful for. This writing of mine in this book helped me back up the downward track of FINALITY. I'm dinged, but OK. I want the same to be true for you, when needed.

As we write together through this book of DOs, DON'Ts and DAREs, this is very good for both of us. When you hit the wall, give in for a bit, like I did, and then review all the good stuff you wrote down in this book, like I did. I know you will be helped by what you, yourself, have written. And the battering, jarring pain of banging into that immovable wall of FINALITY will be lessened. Be encouraged. Continue to write.

Caregivers and Handicappers

At the finish of each section of the 5 Fs of Reaction to Disability, I've asked you to review the F we have just completed. I've asked you to Reflect, Think, Pray, Write, ADAPT. You should be getting good at this by now. So please go ahead and do what you are getting good at. Write down here some ways that you can ADAPT to this irreversible 5th F of FINALITY. And if you have a *Facing It Journal*, begin to daily rank (0–10) and write in that journal concerning the natural reaction of FINALITY. Meaningful and purposeful actions may be getting easier for you. I hope so. Write away.

I can't tell you how relieved I am to be leading into the upcoming 4 Fs that comprise four Good Choices we can make to help us on this wild ride of a lifetime. The four Good Choices involve FAITH • FAMILY • FRIENDS • (and a) FUTURE FACE TO FACE MEETING.

But, before we take this next wonderful upward track that will lead to level ground and a resting place, we need to take a brief look at one more natural human reaction: a reaction that can accompany any one of the 5 Fs of Reaction to Disability, or all of them. DEPRESSION – THE BIG D

THE BIG D

The Big D – DEPRESSION

DEPRESSION – Definition: A severe despondency and dejection typically felt over a period of time and accompanied by feelings of hopelessness and inadequacy.

It just seems so right to talk about DEPRESSION as we complete our list of Reactions to Physical Disability. (Hideous, but appropriate.) Let's quickly look at some DOs, DON'Ts and DAREs concerning the BIG D, because I can't stay here very long and there are many good counselors, doctors, books, and articles to help people get through the BIG D. Remember, I'm no pro. I just know about my own close encounters with DEPRESSION.

DO – Handicappers

DO know that camping out for very long in any one of the 5 Fs of Reaction to Disability will absolutely and for sure throw us out of control and onto the fast track downhill into DEPRESSION. If we allow our human reactions to overpower us, rule us, and push us around the coaster track, we will end up flying off the track at break-neck speed or pile-up in a heap at the bottom of one of the big dips. DO get professional help when needed. DO know we have at least 4 good CHOICES we can make to counter the 5 Fs of Reaction to Physical Disabilities. The 4 Fs of CHOICE are coming up. We have CHOICES to enjoy. Yippee! These 4 Fs of CHOICE make the wild ride worthwhile, doable, and even allow us to help other cappers and caregivers caught in the reaction mode of the 5 Fs. Sigh of relief, from this capper. Literally. Sigh.

> *My up close and personal encounters with DEPRESSION have sifted out into three levels: mild, moderate, and severe. When the BIG D even begins to approach a moderate level, I go looking for help — professional help. This Princess hasn't had to live out a severe level, yet. I've only flirted with it on rare occasions. I hope I never have to live through a severe bout of DEPRESSION. (This is a fervent hope!). But I DO know if I even approach severe levels, I'm heading straight to the pros for help. I'm an amateur. I need someone well trained to assist me out of the BIG D.*

DO know that sometimes it isn't necessarily circumstances that cause DEPRESSION, but sometimes DEPRESSION is a direct result of a body out of whack. Can you tell I'm not a professional? Sometimes medications and the accompanying side effects can bring on the BIG D. Sometimes a chemical imbalance in our bodies can do it. (I don't even want to talk about pre-menopause.) So if you are DEPRESSED, have a physician check you out. Look at the definition one more time.

How about you? Have you experienced this crummy BIG D? Was it mild, moderate, or severe? How did you escape? Are you there now?

 ## DO – Caregivers

DO realize that your capper will almost certainly experience these 5 Fs of Reaction to their disabilities. They may have other reactions I haven't mentioned that are unique to their disabilities. Do realize you, too, will probably experience these 5 Fs as well. What fun. Your capper is going to need you to be on the lookout for them as they maneuver the coaster course of the 5 Fs of Reaction and this BIG D. Your capper needs you to evaluate, assist, love, encourage, and point the way to the upcoming 4 Fs of CHOICE that can literally save both your capper and you from reactions leading to a DEPRESSION disaster. You need to be doubly ready — for us; and for yourself. DO know that you may need to seek professional help, for them, or for yourself, or for the both of you. How do you feel about all this? DEPRESSED? Go ahead and evaluate where you are, and where you think your capper is, concerning the BIG D. As you write, consider the 3 levels of DEPRESSION: mild, moderate, and severe.

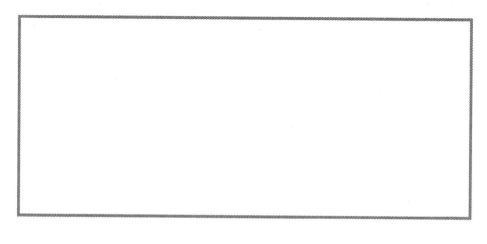

 ## DON'T – Handicappers

DON'T let yourself stay too long in any of the stinky 5 Fs of Reaction to Disability. DON'T. Otherwise, DEPRESSION is a certainty, and the uphill climb out of this BIG D is very difficult at best. I always need help of some kind to escape the Big D.

> *Once again, journaling was a help to me. I'll let you in on my scribbles as I duked it out with the BIG D one day. This is personal stuff. Just between God and you and me. Here's what I wrote on one tough to FACE IT day:*
>
> *— "Know I can't stay here long, but hard to even move this pen on paper, let alone DO anything else. ... Help, Lord, help. I feel totally checked out. Physically/Mentally/Socially/Spiritually/Emotionally .... Almost shut down altogether. Probably a lot of this is hormonal, but it's how I feel. Truly the BIG D: DOWN. DEAD. DISABLED. (duh!) DISTRACTED. DARK. DISMAL. DUMPY. DOWNCAST. DENSE. DISINTERESTED. DISHEARTENED. DISTANT. DISCONNECTED. DISORIENTED. DISAPPOINTED. "DIS"- EVERYTHING! Hard to do anything but try to escape, sleep, hide, get away in my mind, go fetal and stay there." —*

Sound like DEPRESSION to you? Me too. My Lord and my husband helped me out of the pit that day. How I love the both of them! DON'T stay in the dark pit of the BIG D too long. It is too dangerous. Get good help —

professional help when needed. Write down some places you can go to get help and some people who can help. Who ya gonna call?

 DON'T – Caregivers

DON'T let yourself or your capper camp out too long in any of the 5 Fs of Reaction to Disability. DON'T. Or with the certainty mentioned to the cappers, you will both be pitched into a downhill slide that can end in a disaster of deep, lingering, dark DEPRESSION. Please DON'T stay there or allow your capper to stay there. It's too hard to climb up those steep, narrow, coaster tracks made slippery with the BIG D. Please get good, professional help for yourself, your capper, or the both of you.

This is a primary directive. DON'T ignore signs of DEPRESSION. (Note the definition once again.) DON'T. How do you feel?

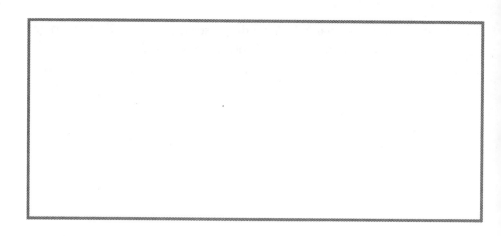

 DARE – Readers

DARE to watch out for yourselves and for each other. Be in tune with each other. Communicate. DARE to be honest about your reactions to the disabilities that have affected your lives. DARE to be aware of the 5 Fs and the natural reactions handicappers and caregivers have concerning them. DARE to FACE IT together and not get tangled up in any one of the 5 Fs of Reaction for too long. You can do it together with appropriate, good help. Say bye-bye to DEPRESSION. And good riddance! How do you feel about honesty and working together? What are you feeling as we come to the end of the 5 Fs and the BIG D? Right now, share it in writing.

Caregivers and Handicappers

I kept the section on DEPRESSION quite short on purpose. I can't hang out there very long even when writing. I must ADAPT and carry on. How about you?

Please Reflect. Think. Pray. Write. ADAPT. You both are equipped with some knowledge now. Use it. Write with me, my Buddies. Use the *Facing It Journal* if you have one, or another of your choosing. Rank (0–10) and write about the Big D. Rest assured, I'm not trying to sell you a specific journal. But I am sharing what I have learned through the process of writing this book: I need to know where I am in my daily Reactions to Disability. The best way to do this is to rank and record my reactions every day. The *Facing It Journal* was my adaptation to **not** wanting to write every day. By using it, I'm able to just check boxes, write if I want, and recognize quickly how I'm handling each day. Whether you have a *Facing It Journal* or not, write your hearts out as you begin to ADAPT to the ever-lurking possibility of DEPRESSION. Meaningful and purposeful actions in this all too personal arena of DEPRESSION are essential. Write.

Okay. This ride is about to get fun. It's time! We're going to look at the beautiful 4 Fs of CHOICE that counter the yucky 5 Fs of Reaction and the Big D. Let's get ready for a challenging, fun, mostly smooth, upward glide on our roller coaster. This ride will end in love, joy, peace, patience, kindness, goodness, faithfulness, gentleness and self-control — life to the fullest. Oh boy! I'm ready! Are you? Here we go!

Part 2

The 4 Fs of Choice:

FAITH · FAMILY · FRIENDS · FUTURE FACE-TO-FACE

> CHOICE – Definition: An act of selecting or making a decision when FACED with two or more possibilities.

The following 4 Fs are CHOICES we can make as handicappers and as caregivers. Positive, helpful, life-changing CHOICES we can make to counter the 5 Fs of Reaction to physical disabilities. (See page **15** for a definition of REACTION.) All of the 4 Fs of CHOICE involve establishing and maintaining good, strong, loving relationships; first with God and then with other human beings.

 Before we begin to take look at the 4 Fs of CHOICE I must issue a WARNING and a PLEA to all readers.

> WARNING – Definition: Cautionary advice, advance notice of something.

> PLEA – Definition: A request made in an emotional and urgent manner.

The WARNING involves the upcoming topic of FAITH. I know that I must caution each of you and give you advance notice that what I have to say in the area of FAITH may provoke strong reactions. You may find what I write to be strange, offensive and exclusive. You may find it new, exciting, and liberating. And some of you will recognize it as familiar, warm and comforting. I have no idea how each of you will respond. But I do have a heartfelt PLEA.

My PLEA is this. Keep reading and writing with me. Keep on interacting and experiencing. Don't quit on me now. There will be practical and personal places to interact with me as we continue to FACE IT together. Please don't refuse to read all of the 4 Fs of CHOICE and the corresponding DOs, DON'Ts and DAREs. I am making this request in an emotional and urgent manner! You just can't hear me. These 4 Fs of CHOICE continue to help me counter the 5 Fs of Reaction and the Big D every day. I want you to have this help as well. So, please continue to interact with this handbook to the end, no matter how you react to FAITH and the following Fs of FAMILY, FRIENDS and a FUTURE FACE-TO-FACE. Will you? Please, cooperate with this Princess and complete your reading and writing. For those of you who are already hesitant to continue after the WARNING, there is at the very least, a reward for the curious. You will find out why I had to have my FACING IT mirror and the full significance of the date and the mirror itself. It is a beautiful, true story.

All right. I have issued the WARNING and the PLEA. It is now my CHOICE to get us rolling on the upward track of the roller coaster. We are now heading towards the end of our trip and an exit from the wild ride of Reactions to Physical Disabilities. Let's see how we can CHOOSE to step out of our cramped little coaster-car onto spacious, flat, high ground. Let's take a look at FAITH, the first of the 4 Fs of CHOICE.

Chapter 6

The 4 Fs of Choice:

FAITH

FAITH – Definition: Complete trust or confidence in someone or something.

That's interesting. Do you, as a capper or a caregiver have FAITH as a reality in your life? Do you completely trust anybody? Do you have complete confidence in anything? Who? What? (By now, you surely know what to do with this empty box.) This is for both handicappers and caregivers.

Please take a look at the definition of FAITH once again. The FAITH that I am referring to in this book, is both FAITH in Someone and in something.

The Someone is Jesus. And the something, is FAITH in the Living Word of God, the Bible. Please don't check out here! You've stuck with me this far. Read to the end of this book of DOs, DON'Ts and DAREs, and **then** decide what to do with the 4 Fs of CHOICE. If you skipped it, go back and read the preceding WARNING and PLEA so you know why I want you to read to the end of this handbook.

The kind of FAITH I'm talking about goes beyond complete trust and confidence in the Someone and the something. This kind of FAITH involves belief and trust and loyalty. With this kind of FAITH you will experience spiritual revelation and spiritual transformation, no matter what you are FACING. These are more than strong and stirring words for me and my caregiver/husband. This FAITH for us means an interactive relationship with the living God that results in love, joy, peace, protection, guidance, help and the beautiful promise of an abundant life lived here on Earth and the wonderful promise of a place of reunion and perfection when we leave this earthly body. Heaven is a certainty for Jim and for me and that makes me smile, even now, as I type away.

In Chapter 2, I told you a bit about who I am and what qualifies me to write about FACING IT. Now I can really express the who, of "who I am." I am a follower of Jesus of Nazareth. A woman who is fully forgiven and fully accepted by the God Who made her. A woman prepared for devastating physical disabilities, by a Lord Who loves and cares for her. A woman who has a vibrant, interactive relationship with the Jesus Who once walked the earth. Amazing? Yes. True? Yes! Is it possible for you, as handicappers and caregivers? YES! This is supernatural stuff I'm talking about. No doubt about it. Want to know more? I hope so, 'cause I'm letting loose.

FAITH – Complete and total belief, trust and loyalty to God and His Living Word, the Bible, is the foundation and stronghold of my life. In this first F of the 4 good CHOICES we can make, I want you to know two things for sure. I know them for sure, and so can you.

First, God wants us to seek Him out and know Him personally. He wants us to seek Him with all our heart and soul and mind and strength. This is His loving desire for us.

Second, as a result of seeking God and getting to know Him and His ways, by looking into the Bible, we can experience daily, loving, interpersonal relationship with the God of the entire universe!

As we actively pursue God, we can talk with Him, and hear Him talk back in a variety of ways. We can trust His voice, always, because He cares for us in ways we cannot even imagine. He cares so much for each one of us that He sent His only Son, Jesus, into this world, to bring light, life, laughter, love, forgiveness, and the offer of eternal life and restoration of relationship with Himself, the Father God of all people.

The A, B, C, D, and E of FAITH

How do we get to this place of FAITH? Good question. You know we've already talked about the 5 stinking Fs of Reaction to Physical Disability and the BIG D. And you know that right now, we are embarking on the upward track of the 4 Fs of CHOICE. These are CHOICES that can help us adjust and ADAPT to whatever physical disabilities we are FACING, as either handicappers or caregivers. Get ready, Readers. I'm going to throw some **more** letters of the alphabet at you — not just Fs. Keep reading.

In order to understand FAITH, I'm going to use the 5 letters of the alphabet that precede the letter F — A, B, C, D, and E. What do these 5 letters have to do with the F, of FAITH? It's now my honor and privilege to guide both handicappers and caregivers through these 5 letters to the best news you've ever heard. With this news you can FACE IT, whatever "IT" is, well. This is the good news spoken and lived out by Jesus of Nazareth — the good news that runs from the very beginning to the very end of the Bible. This is the news that takes a person from spiritual death to spiritual life. This is the best news ever! This is the good news of how to CHOOSE FAITH. When we read a good translation of the Bible (recommended translations are coming up), aspects of God and our possible responses to Him jump out at us. We have the gift of free CHOICE. And there are some really good things to CHOOSE — things that affect our lives now and forever. Here we go with the A, B, C, D, and E CHOICES on the upward track to FAITH!

A. Agree. We can CHOOSE to agree with God that He is perfect and we are not. Huh? Agreeing is harder for some of us than others. At first, I had a real hard time with this. It took quite a while for me to agree. Remember, I *am* the Princess. However, the Bible states the sad truth of our human situation saying, "All have sinned and fallen short of the glory of God." The Bible tells us that God created us to enjoy a wonderful and perfect love relationship with Him forever and ever. He didn't make us automatic-love-Him-back-robots. Instead, He made each person a unique individual, who could CHOOSE to love Him back. We were given freedom to CHOOSE to enjoy a perfect love relationship with the God of all creation. Or, we could CHOOSE to turn our backs to Him and CHOOSE our own ways, not His. Guess what? We have all CHOSEN our own ways at some point and the perfect love relationship with our perfectly wonderful and loving God has been ruined. By us, not Him. We have all turned against His perfect love and perfect ways. There is now a gaping chasm between our loving God and us. Our perfect God can only abide in perfection. And, man, we are not perfect anymore! As soon as we are able, it seems we turn against God and go our own way.

The Bible calls our personal imperfections, sin. Sin is anything we do, say, or think that goes against the will or Word of God. Is anybody reading this perfect? Me neither. Sin damages our relationships with God and with other people. It's not pretty. We're in trouble. This is the "sin thing" that the Bible talks about. We find out that we all have sinned and this sin separates us from God and His incredible, interactive love, now, and forever. And, there's nothing we can do on our own to fix this awful separation. The Bible says that we are spiritually dead in our sin and in our separation from the Author of Life.

So — we can CHOOSE to **A – Agree** with God that He is perfect and we are helplessly imperfect on our own. (This is the bad news part of the good news that's coming up. How can we understand the good news if we don't understand the bad news first?) This CHOICE is mine. This CHOICE is yours. I CHOOSE to AGREE. Do you CHOOSE to **A – Agree** with God that He is perfect and you are not?

B. Believe. We can CHOOSE to believe that Jesus is our Rescuer. Rescuer? From what? Jesus is our Rescuer from the consequence of what we just agreed to — the fact that God's perfect and we're not. (And that consequence is soul separation from God.)

The Bible describes this situation in several ways. One description is a legal picture: our errors, mistakes, and rebellion — our sins, have a penalty associated with them. The just consequence of broken law is for a penalty to be assessed. Another description is an economic one — we receive what we've earned. In this case, our sin earns us a debt we can't repay. Perhaps the clearest picture is that of purity (or holiness in biblical terms). Imagine a container of 100% pure, liquid gold. What could be added to that container that wouldn't change its nature? Only more 100% pure gold. For us to be with God, we need to be like He is when it comes to purity or holiness. Once we've sinned, we're no longer pure.

Penalty, debt, and separation. The Bible says that we are spiritually dead in our sins and are unable to bridge the gap between us and God. So God provided Someone Who paid our penalty, forgave all the debt we owed, and cleaned us up so that we are once again able to be in the presence of our perfect, loving God. The Bible says that Jesus is our Rescuer, Forgiver, Debt-payer, and Restorer of that perfect love relationship we were made for. The Bible also says that Jesus took on the sins of all of humanity when He went to the cross, suffered, died, and was buried. He did all this on purpose so we would have a way back to God. (By the way, three days later He walked out of His tomb, alive and well, to prove He was Who He said He was: the One with authority to forgive sins, the Messiah, God on Earth!)

Jesus' friend John recorded many things Jesus said. You may recognize this quote. Jesus said, "God so loved the world that he gave his only begotten Son, that whoever BELIEVES in him should never die, but have eternal life." (John 3:16). Pam's paraphrase: God loves all people so much that He sent His Son to them. Anybody that truly BELIEVES He is God's Son and their Forgiver will not be separated from God but have spiritual life forever.

In a letter, John later wrote, "If we confess our sins he is faithful and just to forgive us and purify us from all unrighteousness." (1st John 1:9). The "he" in that last sentence refers to Jesus, our Forgiver and Restorer. "Unrighteousness" literally means a condition of not being right with God. Jesus' life, death, and resurrection, prove God's love and power and His desire to have each one of us in close, loving, right relationship with Him now, in the world, and forever, in Heaven.

174

Wow! All we have to do is BELIEVE Jesus is Who He says He is and ask for His forgiveness. Jesus told His followers, "I am the Way, the Truth, and the Life, and no one comes to the Father except through Me." (John 14:6). I know this is true. I BELIEVE it. When we CHOOSE to BELIEVE we experience forgiveness, freedom, and a certainty of spiritual cleanliness and new spiritual life. Please give Jesus a chance to prove Himself to you too, like He proved it to John and to me and to so many others over so many years!

You may be asking, who is this John anyway? He was one of the original 12 followers of Jesus when Jesus was actively teaching and preaching the good news of God. John likes to call himself, "the disciple Jesus loved."(By the way, disciple is another word for follower or student.) John must have felt Jesus' love in a very unique and special way. He was present at the last supper, Jesus' arrest and torture and crucifixion. He was among the first to see and BELIEVE that God had indeed raised Jesus from the dead. John was an eyewitness to the glory of God as Jesus walked the Earth. John is the author of several New Testament books of the Bible including: The Gospel of John, 1st John, 2nd John, 3rd John, and the last book of the Bible, called Revelation. He knew Jesus well and helped to get the good news out to the world.

I want you to find a good study Bible translation if you don't already have one. It's worth the money. I like the *Zondervan NIV Study Bible* or the *NIV Quest Study Bible*, which both use the New International Version translation. My recommendation is that you read the gospel of John (gospel is just a very old word that means good news) in the New Testament, first. Read this gospel of John with an open mind and seek God's Truth with all your heart, soul, mind, and strength. Let the Spirit of the Living Lord convince you of His reality. Then read the three other gospels of Matthew, Mark, and Luke, to get a well rounded account of Who this Jesus is. He is real. Find out for yourself.

We can CHOOSE to **B – Believe** that Jesus is indeed our risen Rescuer, Forgiver, and Restorer. I CHOOSE to BELIEVE. Do you? In the Bible, when people BELIEVED in Jesus they acknowledged their sins, turned away from a self-centered life to a God-centered one, and were baptized as a sign of their new FAITH in Jesus as Forgiver. What do you BELIEVE? Here's a space to write about this CHOICE, any plans you make to explore this letter B of FAITH, and the results of that exploration.

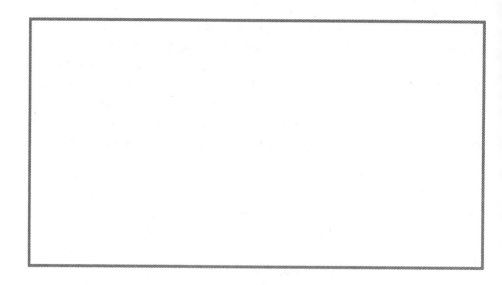

C. Commit. We can CHOOSE to commit our lives to Jesus as our very own Rescuer and Lord. What does this mean?

Well, for sure this is no light commitment. To COMMIT to Jesus as Rescuer and Lord of our lives means we CHOOSE to let Him be the Boss of our lives — every aspect of our lives. You think about that. I'll think about it too. (There are a lot of bad bosses in the world, so it's a good thing He is the best Boss in the universe who always has our best in mind.) When we CHOOSE to ask Jesus to be Lord of our lives and COMMIT our hearts and minds and souls to Him, the Bible says we are "born again." (Look at the Gospel of John chapter 3. Yeah, this is the same John, Jesus' friend.) To be born again means that we are made spiritually alive, whole, clean and new, by the Spirit of God. The Holy Spirit of Jesus Himself enters our very being and we are made spiritually alive! He brings us true refreshment and true freedom. Everyone needs this, but as handicappers and caregivers I think we have a special appreciation for what it means to be whole, clean, new, refreshed, and freed.

Please read the book of John and the other 3 gospels and find out what I'm talking about. But believe me, the Bible, and Jesus — "born again" is the only way to truly live your life now, and ultimately, forever. I challenge you, Dear Readers, to read and see if you are ready to COMMIT your life to the will and the ways of Jesus of Nazareth. I hope you take up this challenge. And I pray you choose to COMMIT to Jesus as Lord of your life.

176

We can CHOOSE to **C – Commit** to Jesus as our very own Forgiver and gladly receive Him as Lord of our lives. I CHOOSE to COMMIT to Him. Are you ready to COMMIT or do you need to take up the challenge of searching Him out in the gospel of John? Do you need to search the other gospels as well? Have you already COMMITTED your life to the One Who wants to be your Forgiver and Lord? Please write. How do you feel about this COMMITMENT?

D. Develop. We can CHOOSE to develop in this new life.

This is a deliberate and important CHOICE to make. As COMMITTED followers of Jesus of Nazareth we need to CHOOSE to grow and mature in our love relationship with the God of the universe and keep on growing and growing until one day, we meet Him face-to-face. How to develop? Good question. We can CHOOSE to **D – Develop** in our faith by joining a Bible-believing church, CHOOSING to serve others in our church and community, CHOOSING to join a Bible study group and continuing to learn about the Bible. What does it say? What does it mean? So what? (How can we apply what we learn to our lives?) In other words, we need to see the Truth, know the Truth, and live the Truth. This DEVELOPMENT takes time and, frankly, it takes effort. It is so worth it! This DEVELOPMENT is essential to our spiritual health. Sometimes this DEVELOPMENT is fun (like when we get to know and enjoy other people as we dig into the Bible together) and sometimes it is difficult (like when we are challenged by what Jesus requires of us and how we must change and grow and ADAPT). This is something of which I am certain: biblical spiritual DEVELOPMENT is essential to our spiritual health. Just as we cannot remain babies in our physical bodies, the Bible teaches us that we are not to remain as infants in our FAITH. Healthy babies naturally grow and mature physically. As much as we might like our little ones to remain innocent babes, they grow into teenagers, and hopefully into happy, healthy adults. As "new creations in Christ Jesus," He allows us the CHOICE to either remain spiritual babies or to grow and DEVELOP in our knowledge and love of God. We need to DEVELOP spiritually every day of our lives. There is always more to learn about God — always more. He is wonderful, fun, funny, awesome, and fascinating! I encourage you to keep on learning.

Have you ever asked why? Why? Why? WHY? Oh yeah. There are so many whys in life. Here are just a few: Why is there pain? Why is there suffering? Why am I disabled? Why has someone I love so much been so handicapped that now I am the assigned caregiver? Why am I reading this book?

Why don't you take a few minutes and write down some of your WHYs right now? Don't get discouraged, just write down some of your WHYs in this box and then read my own personal box.

As I learned about God in the Bible, I learned about others and myself and God's whole amazing plan for each one of us in His creation. In the learning process I was helped in this area of "WHY?" My CHOICE to grow and learn and DEVELOP in my knowledge of God and His Book, the Bible, literally saved my hide in the WHY department. In the 14 years since I recognized Jesus as my Rescuer and my Lord, I've come to know Him well enough that WHY is no longer an issue in my life.

Through the work of His Spirit in me and my growing knowledge of Him and His ways, I know He has a good purpose for my handicaps and any other trials or blessings that come my way. I completely trust God as I come to know Him better and better. What I've learned over years of DEVELOPMENT is that God is faithful and His love for me endures forever. I really don't need to know all the WHYS of my disabilities and troubles. I just need to know the Who in charge of my WHYS, and allow Him to DEVELOP in me the qualities He desires. His will and His ways are the very best for me, and I know it. What peace and joy and freedom accompany the growing knowledge of God.

I recommend three good resources for you to take advantage of as you pursue growth and DEVELOPMENT in your FAITH.

Your #1 resource is always your Bible. Always go there first. No matter what. As I said before, I prefer the *Zondervan NIV Study Bible* or the *NIV Quest Study Bible*. Both have helped me continue to grow in knowledge and love of my Lord. Your Bible is God's Word: the most important textbook in the world.

If you are new to FAITH, or have not yet named Jesus as Forgiver and Lord, there is a fun, user-friendly book of information called, *Bruce & Stan's Guide to God*, by Bruce Bickel and Stan Jantz (this book has been reissued as *Knowing God 101*). I have learned and laughed out loud as I've read this book. They address topics such as: What is God like? The Three-in-Oneness of God. Angels. Satan. Demons. Sin. (You're kind of familiar with that one already). Heaven. Hell. And so much more. It is a fun, informed, good read. I recommend it highly to you that are new believers or to you who are curious, but not ready to AGREE, BELIEVE, or COMMIT as yet. Enjoy!

If you are a follower of Jesus and have never participated in the workbook study called *Experiencing God*, by Henry Blackaby and Claude King, get it in your mitts and get to work! These authors help others learn how to listen for the voice of God and see His Presence in every day life. They teach, by Scripture, how much God desires a love relationship with each person and how that knowledge can change our lives. They teach us how to look and listen for God's active invitation to join with Him in accomplishing His good and perfect will here on earth. This was, and continues to be, a life-changing study for me, and for countless others. I go back to my workbook often, and am astounded at the depth of insight and knowledge within its pages. I strongly recommend this workbook study. You will be blown away by new ways of understanding Who God is, how He communicates with us, and how much He loves us and wants us to love Him back.

It's our CHOICE. We can CHOOSE to grow and DEVELOP in our FAITH. I CHOOSE to keep on growing in my understanding of God and His loving plans for me and for others. Will you CHOOSE to DEVELOP too? What specific action could you now take to enhance your DEVELOPMENT?

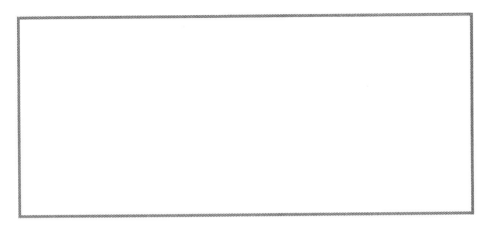

E. Evangelize. We can CHOOSE to evangelize: to tell others about our FAITH.

If you have come as far as this, through the A, B, C, and D of FAITH, you will be ready to tell others about the difference Jesus has made in your life. We have good news to share, the best news to share! Sharing the good news of Jesus, as my Living Forgiver and Lord, is what EVANGELISM is all about. It's my story of coming to understand Who this Jesus is. It's your story of coming to understand Who this Jesus is. It's the telling of how He's changed our lives through His forgiveness and restored our love relationship with God. It's fun! It's exciting! It's essential to tell others the good news of Who Jesus is!

I CHOOSE to **E – Evangelize**. I love to tell others about the One Who brought true Life into my life! I love to talk about Jesus and how much He loves me and each and every person. I love to share the good news of my reconciliation to my loving Father God.

I'm often asked how I can remain "so happy and upbeat" when I'm so obviously handicapped and physically dinged. I always respond with a question back to the questioner: "Do you really want to know?" If the questioner answers, "Yes," I ask, "Are you sure?" If they answer, "Yes," again, they get to hear the good news of Jesus. (They asked for it!) This is the good news that has been shared one-on-one ever since He walked the earth. It isn't hard. It's as natural as breathing since His Spirit lives within me. Each and every follower of Jesus of Nazareth has an on-going, personal, love relationship with Him. Who doesn't want to share a relationship as exciting and fulfilling as this with others thirsty for a taste

181

of Truth and Everlasting Life? These questioners always receive a study Bible for their very own, so they can begin pursuing the good news for themselves.

There are many simple ways to demonstrate and share your FAITH. A sincere smile for someone who looks discouraged, a "God bless you" when someone sneezes, an offer to pray for someone in distress, and on and on …. A simple way to tell others your story is to keep the ABCDEs in mind and then:

Tell what your life was like before you Agreed, Believed, and Committed.

Tell why you decided to Agree, Believe, and Commit.

Tell what your life is like now that you are doing ABCDEs.

Does this make sense? Will you CHOOSE to EVANGELIZE with me, and spread the good news of God's great love for every person, through Jesus, His Son? Will you CHOOSE TO E – **Evangelize**? Write your Jesus story in the box. Try to keep it short and sweet so you can easily share it with others. (If you haven't made your way to FAITH yet, you may skip this box for now, but I hope you come back to it later.)

Whew. There you have the A, B, C, D, and E of FAITH. We've worked our way through the alphabet to F again: FAITH. Following are some DOs, DON'Ts and DAREs concerning FAITH in Jesus. You'll see how the CHOICE of FAITH practically and specifically helps counteract the 5 Fs of Reaction to Physical Disability, and the Big D. This is good stuff. Keep reading and writing.

 DO – Readers

DO CHOOSE FAITH in the person of Jesus the Christ and FAITH in the Living Word of God, the Bible. DO CHOOSE to establish and maintain a relationship with the Lord of the entire universe. Please DO.

> *As you've read (and written) your way through this handbook, I have shared my own personal handicapped experiences with you. I've often asked you, as either handicappers or caregivers, to write down your responses and hopefully share them with each other. As we consider this DO of FAITH in Jesus, as Lord and Rescuer, and the DO of FAITH in the written Word of God, the Bible, I have to tell you all that this is the most important DO of all the DOs we've considered so far. I know that this DO has eternal consequences, as well as huge benefits in the now of our lives. As a result, I have to tell you that as I sit here at my desk I feel a huge responsibility to let you know how important this FAITH is to me, and how important this FAITH is to you.*

Since we've taken a look at John, as Jesus' follower, friend and eyewitness, I'd like to stick with him for the following examples of why my FAITH in Jesus, and His Word, is the very foundation of my hope, joy, peace, and life. As I'm sure you well remember, we have already worked our way through the 5 awful Fs of Reaction to Disability, as well as the BIG D. I want to show you how helpful Jesus and His Word can be as we FACE each of these nasty 5 Fs of Reaction and the BIG D, Depression. (There are 66 books in the Bible, but we are going to just hang out in John's eyewitness account of Jesus.) Following, are examples of how God has helped me, as I read the book of John, and considered each of the 5 Fs and the BIG D. Please DO take a look at these brief examples of how FAITH continues to help this handicapper deal with my ongoing challenges. (Caregivers, DO take note as well) John was an eyewitness and an inspired writer. Let's look at what John has to say to us today as we FACE IT together, with FAITH at center stage.

FAILURE

As my body FAILS me, I can do less and less in the way of physical activity. This dismays me as well as my caregivers. But John 6:28-29 tells us how Jesus answered the people that were asking Him questions about the work that God requires. John writes: "Then they asked him, 'What must we do to do the works God requires?' Jesus answered, 'The work God requires is this: to believe in the one he has sent.'"

OK. What's the work that God requires according to Jesus? The work required is to believe in the One God sent: that would be Jesus. Now, this is work I can do! No physical labor is required, only FAITH. This is the FAITH that helps me experience spiritual transformation and strength regardless of my physical FAILURES. And don't take this lightly. Often, FAITH takes work. Lots of work. But as a handicapper, it is work I can throw myself into without risk of bodily injury — to myself or an innocent bystander. Are you willing to do the work that God requires? FAILURE will fly out the window if you're willing. Are you willing?

FRUSTRATION

John also writes in his gospel account, of the time Jesus spent with His closest disciples in an "upper room" during the last meal Jesus would eat with them before his terrible physical suffering and crucifixion began. In chapters 13 and 14, Jesus intimately teaches His followers many things. He also predicts His betrayal by Judas Iscariot, and Peter's upcoming denials of Jesus as his Lord — three denials in a row. I feel for Peter. Jesus tells them that where He is about to go, they cannot follow. How

184

FRUSTRATING! They've been closely following Him for about three years. They love Him and want Him close by. He is their teacher, master, friend, Messiah. And now, He's telling them all this confusing, distressing, disturbing stuff. FRUSTRATION is natural, but here is Jesus' response to the group's distress and Peter's questioning: "Do not let your hearts be troubled. Trust in God; trust also in Me."

OK. This can apply to me as well. As a handicapper I can get confused, distressed and disturbed. This can translate into FRUSTRATION in my case too. What can I do according to Jesus? I can CHOOSE to trust in God and in Jesus as well. What does this mean? Just what it says: trust, calm down, relax, and lie back into God's hands and trust His ways for me. God Himself helps me in this trust and when I let Him, He can send FRUSTRATION flying, and replace that reaction with peace, in trust. Wow!

To trust someone implies you know that someone. How can you get to know Jesus so you can trust Him? Will you let Him help you in the midst of FRUSTRATION?

FURY

As a handicapper, FURY can come at me like a Tasmanian devil. And I'm ashamed to say, I can sometimes act like one too. I go my own stubborn, stupid ways, and end up in an angry dead-end. In chapter 6 of John's Gospel, a lot of "grumbling" goes on near the end of the chapter. Jesus teaches the truth about Himself and there are a lot of unhappy campers. He teaches about His relationship with His Father and what is expected from anyone who would truly want to follow Him. He teaches some difficult stuff and some of those who had been following Him quit in apparent anger and disgust. My guess is that they are FURIOUS with Him and what He has just said. Listen to John 6:66-69: "From this time many of his disciples turned back and no longer followed him. 'You do not want to leave too, do you?' Jesus asked the Twelve. Simon Peter answered him, 'Lord, to whom shall we go? You have the words of eternal life. We believe and know that you are the Holy One of God.'"

I love these words of confession and FAITH that Peter speaks. I need to remember them when I get so angry with this spazzy body and one-eyed face. When FURY kicks me in the stomach, I need to absolutely know there is a Person I can run to for comfort and help. To whom shall I go? My Lord. Why? Because He has the words of eternal life and I know and believe that Jesus is the Holy One of God. No one can take His place. No one can stop the storm of FURY like He can. He is my ever-present place and Person of peace. He can be yours as well, you handicappers and caregivers.

When you are FURIOUS whom do you go to for help? Have you ever asked Jesus to help? What happened?

FEAR

FEAR is a fact of life for many of us handicappers who must constantly depend on others for physical assistance. I'm sure you caregivers can name a few FEARS of your own. How can we deal with this, sometimes, overwhelming sense of FEAR? John and the other disciples experienced quite a thriller of their own. The following account of John, the eyewitness, takes place in the book of John in chapter 6. Jesus was teaching His

186

disciples (He does this all the time) and had climbed up a mountainside to sit down with them. He sees more than 5,000 people coming toward Him. He knows these people are hungry and asks one of the disciples, Philip, how in the world can enough food be provided for this many hungry people? Philip doesn't come up with the correct answer. The other disciples are also unsure of how to proceed, but Jesus isn't. He accepts 5 small barley loaves and 2 small fish from a boy in the crowd. He then gives thanks to God for the itty-bitty amount of food offered, and promptly feeds the entire crowd as much as they could eat. And there were leftovers! Can you picture this humongous picnic, sparked by the offering of one small boy and multiplied by the hands of Jesus? (We aren't to the scary part yet, just hang in here with me a little bit longer.)

All in this huge crowd were eyewitnesses to the miracle of full tummies for everyone and leftovers, to boot. The crowd then intended to come at Jesus and make Him king by force. Who could blame them? But Jesus, knowing what the crowd intended to do, withdrew to a mountain by Himself. (He knew God had other plans for His life.) Are you ready for the scary part, now? All right.

Here it is. John 6:16-21: "When evening came, his disciples went down to the lake, where they got into a boat and set off across the lake for Capernaum. By now it was dark, and Jesus had not yet joined them. A strong wind was blowing and the waters grew rough. When they had rowed three or three and a half miles, they saw Jesus approaching the boat, walking on the water; and they were terrified. But he said to them, 'It is I; don't be afraid.' Then they were willing to take him into the boat, and immediately the boat reached the shore where they were heading."

I can really relate to this. I have felt helpless at the oars, far from a safe shore, with a strong wind blowing, in the midst of rough waters, in the dark. Have you? These 12 disciples had to be scared spitless by the physical forces pushing them around. Wind and waves were rough and they were probably soaked and spooked and pretty desperate for help as they kept on rowing and rowing. I've felt like this. Have you? And, just when they probably thought it was as scary as it could get, FEAR really kicked in. They were not only soaked, scared, and desperate for help, but now they were terrified! Oh man, who or what did they see coming at them walking on the deep, rough, wind-driven waters? A ghost? An apparition? Who? What? They were scared out of their minds! It appeared to be a man walking on the water! Double, triple, quadruple FEAR. (I'm getting a little jittery just thinking about this scene. Especially, since it takes place in the dark.)

Are you getting just a taste of the FEAR they must have been feeling? All physical control of their personal situation was out of their hands. (You and me, too?) Helpless on the water, in a storm, and someone or something that looked like a man was coming at them, walking on the water! Yikes! How did they see Him in the dark of the storm? I don't know. But in the midst of their panic and terror, a familiar voice speaks, "It is I; don't be afraid." They know this voice. They know Who this is. They are eyewitnesses to His awesome power. They trust this One they know as Lord. They let Him into the floundering boat and John says that **immediately** the boat reached the safety of the shore towards which they were headed.

Whenever I am afraid and FEAR assaults me, as I FACE my physical handicaps, I remember this scene. I see my Lord coming to my aid, both physically and supernaturally in the midst of my FEAR storm. I, like John and the others in that boat, can hear Jesus say to me, "It is I; don't be afraid." And if I CHOOSE to, I let Him get into my boat of FEAR and carry me safely to shore. And when I let Him, He always does. I am an eyewitness to His deliverance from my own overwhelming FEARS. He can walk on water. He is in charge. And He is to be trusted with my well being. FEAR melts away in His Presence.

Have you ever let Jesus climb into your FEAR boat? What happened next?

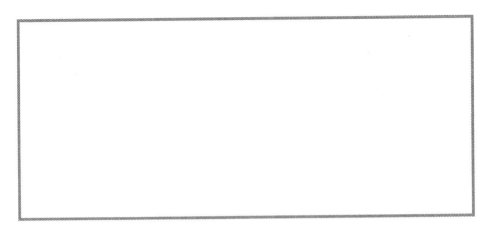

FINALITY

This Princess is stuck with physical handicaps and so is my caregiver husband, who is stuck with me. Are you stuck, too? It isn't pleasant. Our buddy John has something to report on this Reaction to Disability, FINALITY, as well. I'm looking now at chapter 16 of the book of John. The scene is once again, back in that upper room, during the last meal Jesus would share with His closest followers before His betrayal and suffering. During this special meal He was still teaching the ones He loved. Jesus was telling John and the others, that life was about to get tough for them. And that soon, anyone who killed them would think they were offering a service to God. He was warning them of certain hardships to come. FINALITY. And the kicker — He told them that He would soon be leaving planet earth. He was going away. FINALITY.

How awful this had to sound to them! And they were filled with unspeakable grief. But, Jesus assured them that it was best for Him to leave them and go back to His Father in Heaven, because He would leave His very own Spirit with them here on earth. They were still filled with grief. They didn't understand what He was saying. Who would? They just didn't want Him to leave them. FINALITY was staring them in the FACE. That hideous, immoveable, graffiti covered wall of FINALITY was all they could see. Pain. Grief. Loss. The One they knew as God on earth was about to leave them. And their very lives were about to be in danger! Through their grief at His words, He continued to teach. He taught them and He teaches us, about our human reaction to FINALITY. At the end of chapter 16 Jesus says to them, and to us, "I have told you these things, so that in me you

189

may have peace. In this world you will have trouble. But take heart! I have overcome the world."

Did you hear that? Did I hear that? Did they hear that? This is part of the good news — a big part. No matter what is written on the immovable wall of FINALITY, Jesus told them and is telling us, that in Him, we may have peace. Peace. Peace in the FACE of FINALITY. Jesus also said that in this world, there is trouble. Can we agree? Oh yeah, there is trouble. In fact trouble with a capital T — Trouble. I'm living it and so are you. But, and there's a "but" coming. A huge "but!" This "but" makes all the difference in the world as they and we slam into FINALITY. What does Jesus say next? "But take heart! I have overcome the world." We can take heart! Someone has overcome the world. Someone has overcome the awful wall. That Someone is Jesus. Yippee! And He promises peace for any who will seek that peace in Him, the Overcomer for us all.

I know this peace in the FACE of FINALITY. When I CHOOSE to take Jesus at His word, and seek Him as my peace, the ugly wall of FINALITY shrinks to a little bump on the road. Truly! The peace that Jesus brings, as Overcomer, passes all human understanding. I am carried away to peace by my Overcomer. You can be too. Take Him at His Word.

Will you take Him at His Word? Will you let Him be your Overcomer? What do you need Him to overcome in your life?

DEPRESSION

The BIG D — who hasn't experienced this lovely Reaction to Disability, either as the handicapper or the caregiver? I can hear your answers from here. Remember when I let you read a bit of my journaling at a time the BIG D had me down? "Dark" was one of my prime descriptions. I know myself pretty well, by now. I don't like the dark. I don't like to be alone in the dark. I don't want to experience the darkness of DEPRESSION for very long, or that BIG D will grab me in a strangle-hold, gag and bind me, and throw me sliding down the slippery track, into a dark, dungeon of DEPRESSION. I say give me light, and plenty of it! Please! (This makes sense, doesn't it? A Princess naturally loves all things bright and sparkly. I'm looking into my FACING IT mirror right now. And I say the brighter, the better, for this Princess.) Listen to just a little of what our dear John has written that can apply to us as we FACE the BIG D and the deep, dark feelings that accompany DEPRESSION.

John was among many people listening to Jesus teach, and he reported an astounding claim made by his friend, teacher, and Lord. Here is what John wrote in John 8:12: "When Jesus spoke again to the people, he said, 'I am the light of the world. Whoever follows me will never walk in darkness, but will have the light of life." In the eighth chapter of John, as Jesus taught about Who He is, some people verbally challenged His claims. Some were just plain confused. Some believed He was indeed, Who He said He was. And some picked up rocks to throw in an attempt to kill Him. Which course of action do you CHOOSE?

You know me, I CHOOSE to believe what he said about Who He is. He has indeed proven Himself to be my light of life every, I say, *every* time I CHOOSE to closely follow Him. I get into dark trouble when I lose sight of my Lord of Light and Life. Closely following is necessary and so beautifully beneficial.

Listen to John 12:44-46, as John describes Jesus' impassioned plea to His own people (and to us) to believe in Him and also in the One Who sent Him (that would be God). And please note **why** it is so important to Him,

191

for any within earshot to BELIEVE what He is saying: "Then Jesus cried out, 'When a man believes in me, he does not believe in me only, but in the one who sent me. When he looks at me, he sees the one who sent me. I have come into the world as a light, so that no one who believes in me should stay in darkness.'" Did you catch WHY it was so important to Jesus that they (and we) BELIEVE what He said? I think He desperately wanted them (and us) to understand that He is the exact representation of God on earth, the Light of Life, Who alone is able to bring people out of darkness. No wonder He raised His voice and literally cried out. He wanted no one to miss what He was saying! Anyone who truly BELIEVES in Jesus will not "stay in darkness." He is the Light Who will love, help, guide, protect, and push back the darkness for any who BELIEVE that He is Who He claims to be.

I know that when I am DEPRESSED, I often linger and languish in darkness for a while. Like a sailboat caught in the doldrums, it's hard to make myself even want to make a move out of the darkness of DEPRESSION when I'm there. The good news is once again the good news of Who Jesus is. He is my Light. All I need to do is whisper to Him for help, and He has promised to always help, always answer, and pour His pure light all over me. Inside and out. I do not have to "stay in darkness," I have a Rescuer. All I have to do is BELIEVE what He said, and take Him at His Word. I do. And He does. He will shine His beautiful Light on you as well, if you only BELIEVE. He, Himself, is our Way out of darkness into God's wonderful light. What an indescribable gift! How I love the Light of the world! He is my ever-present perfect light. He can be yours, too.

I know we are spending a lot of time dealing with the BIG D here, but I think it is vital to our survival as handicappers and caregivers, to absolutely know, we have instant, ever-ready, loving, all-powerful, help available, in the person of Jesus of Nazareth, His Father, and His Holy Spirit, when DEPRESSION strikes. (And you know it will.) So, here is one more example of how Jesus takes care of us even on our deepest, darkest days. The following account from our friend John is one of my all-time favorites.

We will be looking at chapter 11 of John, and the death of Jesus' good friend, Lazarus. Death. Dark and DEPRESSING. Nothing left. No life. No love. No hope. No recourse. No tomorrows left for the dead one wrapped in grave clothes and laid in a tomb of rock ... or is there?

Sometimes I feel like I am wrapped in grave clothes on my bad days. All I want to do is lie down and stay alone in a cave of DEPRESSION. Darkness holds me tight and I give in. I feel useless, dead, and rotten; at least for a while. The reason I don't ever totally give in and give up and stay there, is made evident from the eyewitness report written down by John.

In a nutshell, here's what happened as reported by John in chapter 11 of his account. Jesus had three good friends He loved very much. Mary, Martha and their brother, Lazarus, all lived in Bethany, a village about two miles from Jerusalem. Jesus had recently left Jerusalem and was teaching on the east side of the Jordan River, about a day's walk from Jerusalem. One day, word came to Jesus that His good friend Lazarus was very sick and the sisters wanted Him to come and help their brother. Jesus purposely delayed the walk to Bethany to help Lazarus. In fact, by the time the messenger reached Jesus, poor Lazarus had probably already died. His body was tenderly cleaned, spiced, wrapped tightly in grave clothes, and laid in a cave-tomb, with a large rock covering the entrance. Lazarus had been dead for four days before Jesus showed up. There was a whole lot of wailing and mourning going on, for good reason. Death and darkness consumed the hearts of friends and relatives who had loved this man.

Especially his sisters. Their brother was dead. They'd grown up together. Maybe they'd patted his baby back waiting for a burp, bathed his chubby baby body, watched him crawl, held his little hand in theirs when he took his first steps, kissed away his "owies," and put him to sleep at night after evening prayers. We don't know for sure the ages of these siblings, so maybe he was their big brother, who took care of them. But we know for certain, that as adults, these three lived together in a town called Bethany. They must have known each other's daily routines. They were familiar with each other's habits. They knew the certain scent of each other's hair and clothes. They must have shared meals and laughter. And I'm sure they knew how to "push each others buttons," and there were moments of discord that are natural to any sibling relationship. But, oh God! Their brother was dead! Dead. And the only One Who could have helped; Who loved him too, had not run the dusty road to their house fast enough. Their brother was dead.

Lazarus was tightly wrapped in the darkness that eventually visits every human being — death. And because they loved their brother, his sisters felt the dark brush of those wrappings touch their hearts with loss and grief.

But then, the Light arrived. The sisters both knew that if Jesus had been there, He could have easily healed their brother. And in their sorrow, they said as much to Him. I really want to let John tell the story from here.

John 11:32-44 — "When Mary reached the place where Jesus was and saw him, she fell at his feet and said, 'Lord, if you had been here, my brother would not have died.' When Jesus saw her weeping and the Jews who had come along with her also weeping, he was deeply moved in spirit and troubled. 'Where have you laid him?' he asked.

'Come and see, Lord,' they replied.

Jesus wept.

Then the Jews said, 'See how he loved him!' But some of them said, 'Could not he who opened the eyes of the blind man have kept this man from dying?'

Jesus, once more deeply moved, came to the tomb. It was a cave with a stone laid across the entrance. 'Take away the stone,' he said.

'But, Lord,' said Martha, the sister of the dead man, 'by this time there is a bad odor, for he has been there four days.'

Then Jesus said, 'Did I not tell you that if you believed, you would see the glory of God?'

So they took away the stone. Then Jesus looked up and said, 'Father, I thank you that you have heard me. I knew that you always hear me, but I said this for the benefit of the people standing here, that they may believe that you sent me.'

When he had said this, Jesus called in a loud voice, 'Lazarus, come out!' The dead man came out, his hands and feet wrapped with strips of linen, and a cloth around his face.

Jesus said to them, 'Take off the grave clothes and let him go.'"

Wow!. What a scene. Can't you see it as breaking news if it happened today? I'd videotape the news-feed and just watch it over and over and over again. But I don't have to. This scene is made fresh in my mind every time I read John's eyewitness account. I sense the scene as Jesus comes upon the wailing mourners. I love Him so much for weeping with them at the grim, relentless, grip of death. (He is soon to feel that darkness Himself.) As He approaches the stench of the tomb and the rock separating Him from His dead friend, again, He is deeply moved and troubled by the touch of death and the pain of separation from a loved one. (Jesus was FACING a stone-covered tomb that held the body of one He loved. He was there. I've been there. Have you been there?) He FACED death straight on. And then He took action.

There were many eyewitnesses there that day. Oh, how I would love to have been one of them. At His command, the stone was removed. Can you imagine the electricity in the air as all waited with bated breath to see what would happen next? What was Jesus going to do? I'm not a betting woman, but I'm willing to bet a decaf-non-fat-sugar-free-hazelnut-latte, that no one thought He was going to holler out Lazarus' name and wait for His friend to exit the tomb! The mourners gathered there had to be in stun-mode. They heard The Voice of Authority call out the dead from the grave. They witnessed death and darkness back off. They got to help Lazarus out of his grave clothes. As he felt the grave clothes being removed, what did Lazarus think? Whose FACE do you think he looked for first, as the cloth was removed from his face? Can you sense the wonder and joy exchanged in that FACE-TO-FACE reunion there in front of a grave that still stank of death? Now there were tears of joy. The sisters were rejoicing! Their brother was alive again! Once dead, now alive at the Master's call! They had their brother back! (I want to clap and jump for joy! Maybe they all did.) What a trip! To the dark, still grave, and then back to life! And Lazarus was now a walking, talking, witness to Who Jesus was (and is), as he resumed life in Bethany with his two happy sisters.

Do you know where I'm going with this? Probably. Even though I haven't physically died, I have felt the near-death, darkness of DEPRESSION. I have been in the cave, withdrawn from family and friends. And I've felt the stone of separation as I've had to FACE the stinking reality of disability. Oh yes, I have.

But ... I have also heard the Voice of Authority call into my darkness, "Pamela, come out!" Oh yes, I have. I have responded to that Voice, and been spiritually set free from all that tightly binds me. Often, I have stumbled out of the dark cave into the arms of Light. Wonder of Wonders! Jesus **is** the Light that can dispel DEPRESSION and death and darkness. I can freely breathe in clean, fresh air and be revitalized by the One Who is Light. All I have to do is BELIEVE and respond to His Voice calling me out. You can too. Please write your name here: "_____, come out!" Will you leave your darkness and fall into the arms of the Son of God? Will you allow the things that bind you to be removed? Oh, what rejoicing will take place! Oh, what freedom waits.

DO CHOOSE FAITH in the Person of Jesus the Christ and FAITH in the Living Word of God, the Bible. Please DO. He is the Way, the Truth, and the Life, and the Light. He really is. Will you write your response in this box?

DON'T – Readers

DON'T turn your back on God and His Word. DON'T refuse the best gift ever offered each human being — a restored love relationship with the Living God through the sacrifice and resurrection of His Son, Jesus the Forgiver. Please DON'T turn your back on abundant life now, and eternal life forever, in Heaven.

There is another huge reason for the DON'T in this section on FAITH. Something I haven't really addressed yet. Actually, it is a someone, I haven't spoken of yet. His name is Satan, "the lord of the flies." He is the author of deception, darkness, and death. He is the tempter, the lover of evil, and the father of lies. He is the spiritual archenemy of our lives and souls. The Bible makes it very clear, that without the protection of Jesus as our Lord and Savior, we are fair game for this evil one and his dark helpers. We are defenseless on our own and we're on our own because of that sin separation from God. Satan is way more powerful than any human being. The Bible says that he is like a roaring lion constantly on the prowl for those he can devour.

Satan and his helpers do their best to keep anyone from BELIEVING in Jesus, because Jesus can send him running away from us by His presence in our lives. Satan loves to deceive, lie, manipulate, tempt, ruin, hurt, and kill. He is a fallen angel who took many other fallen angels with him when God threw him out of Heaven, for trying to be like God. The angels in Heaven were given a CHOICE, just like us. Satan rebelled against God's perfection and attempted to usurp God's position. Big mistake. It cost him Heaven, just like it can cost us Heaven. He continued in his rebellion, and so did Satan's crowd. They continue to defy God to this day and want to take as many human beings with them as they can to a place reserved for them and anyone else they can coerce — Hell. Hell is a place reserved for Satan and his dark angels. It is a certain destination for those who reject God's Son, Jesus. It is a place of eternal separation from the perfect God of love. I DON'T want to go there. You DON'T want to go there.

There is a spiritual battle going on all around us — each one of us. A battle we can't see with human eyes. It is a battle for our very lives, with eternal consequences. Here on earth, in the midst of spiritual warfare, Jesus *will* defend us from evil as we CHOOSE to BELIEVE. God and Satan are not equal contenders. The Bible teaches us that Jesus is God and Satan is just a very evil angel. Jesus is creator; Satan is a created being who made a bad CHOICE. We need Jesus as our defender against evil. (Check out *Bruce & Stan's Guide to God* a.k.a. *Knowing God 101*, for lots more info.) Please, take my advice on this one. DON'T deny Jesus His rightful place as Rescuer and Lord in your life. He is our invincible Defender against the evil one and his dark cohorts. (Look in your Study Bible at what the apostle Paul wrote concerning this topic. Read Ephesians 6:10-18. This will give you an idea as to what we are up against, and Who our protector is.) It is important to note, that even we who BELIEVE in and follow Jesus, can be attacked by this enemy. But, we can CHOOSE to call for back-up, and our Lord will immediately respond and rout this evil angel and his dark helpers for us. Thank God.

Please DON'T refuse His help. What is your response?

 DARE – Readers

The DARE is on! DARE to CHOOSE to **Agree**, **Believe**, **Commit**, **Develop**, and **Evangelize**. To be one who follows Jesus of Nazareth is the biggest DARE of all time. And the most exciting relationship life offers, now and forever. CHOOSE FAITH!

Are you in the process of CHOOSING FAITH in Jesus? Have you already CHOSEN? Do you enjoy a close relationship with Him? Who is Jesus to you? Go ahead and write.

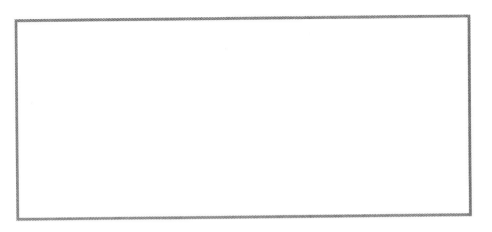

There you have the A, B, C, D, and E of FAITH. Isn't it amusing that the letter F comes after these 5 letters? The letter F has figured hugely in this book so far, and will continue to do so as we consider FAMILY, FRIENDS, and a FUTURE FACE TO FACE.

Handicappers and Caregivers

Journaling about CHOICE is slightly different than journaling about REACTION. That makes sense, doesn't it? CHOICE happens before the fact, and REACTION takes place afterwards. When it comes to CHOICES, writing in your journal is essential. When you journal about a CHOICE, instead of doing a 0–10 ranking, you write a brief plan for what you CHOOSE to do that day. And when I say brief, I mean brief. My plan is usually just a simple to-do list for the day. This first step of recording your plan for the day helps you to actually make a CHOICE. Once you've written that plan in your journal, make sure you do it during the day. Finally, it's still important to record the results of your CHOICE — your thoughts, observations, and feelings about your experiences for the day.

Here's one extra tip when it comes to journaling about FAITH. You can mark down an **A** if you are in the process of trying to **Agree** that God is perfect and you aren't. And write, if you want, what questions you may have, what sources you can use to find answers, how you feel about this **A** of FAITH. Or maybe you are a couple of letters further into FAITH, and are really working on **C – Commit**. You can write a **C** in the FAITH area of the journal page, and then write about what's happening — maybe your successes and failures to truly let Jesus be the Boss.

The *Facing It Journal* has a FAITH section, and a reminder to plan it, do it, and record it. It can help you chart where you are daily in this life-long process of FAITH. This is valuable stuff to know as you FACE the 5 Fs of Reaction and the BIG D.

Plan it. Do it. Record it.

Caregivers and Handicappers

Will you please reflect, think, pray, write, and ADAPT concerning this CHOICE of FAITH? Are you involved right now in any of these letters of FAITH? Which ones? Do you have questions? Can you find answers?

[ ]

You can chart your progress in any of these letters A, B, C, D, or E of FAITH using your own journal, or your *Facing It Journal* if you have one. It's time to add journaling about this CHOICE of FAITH to your daily routine.

We are now ready to move onto another one of the 4 good Fs of CHOICE that will help us FACE our IT. The F that follows FAITH will help keep us on the track that leads to solid, stable ground as handicappers and caregivers. This second F of CHOICE is FAMILY.

Chapter 7

The 4 Fs of Choice:

FAMILY

> FAMILY – Definition: A group of people related to one another
> by blood or marriage; a person or people related to one and so
> to be treated with a special loyalty or intimacy.

FAMILY. Maybe you have one and maybe you don't. Maybe you have good relationships with your FAMILY, maybe you don't. Maybe you are in the midst of raising small children or teens or maybe you are parents of grown up children. Maybe you have the immense fun and privilege of being grandparents. Maybe you don't. Maybe all of your FAMILY lives close and you see them often. Maybe you enjoy this. Maybe you don't. Maybe you are single or a single parent. Maybe you are all alone in this world. Maybe all your FAMILY is estranged or dysfunctional. Maybe none are still on earth.

All I know is that good, strong, consistent, healthy, FAMILY connections and support are essential to the well-being of both handicappers and caregivers. The more interactions the better. What to do if the FAMILY you are born into is unacceptable to you or unaccepting of you? What to do if you have no FAMILY present to help you navigate the roller coaster ride of those 5 stinky Fs of Reaction to Physical Handicaps and the BIG D? What to do? Good questions!

DO – Readers

DO know that even if you enjoy good, strong, consistent, healthy FAMILY connections, you can always benefit from additional close relationships. DO know that even if you come from a dysfunctional, distant, uncomfortable, or even non-existent FAMILY, you can become a welcome, loved and cared for member of a vital, vibrant, caring, supportive, active FAMILY. This CHOICE of FAMILY relationships is yours to make.

Listen to what John wrote in his gospel concerning the BELIEF in, and acceptance of, Jesus as Rescuer. John 1:12-13: "… to all who believed Him and accepted Him, He gave the right to become children of God. They are reborn. This is not a physical birth resulting from human passion and plan — this rebirth comes from God." Did you hear what John just said? When we BELIEVE in, and receive Jesus as our Rescuer and Lord, we are born into a new FAMILY. A spiritual FAMILY. A FAMILY of FAITH. A FAMILY of believers in, and followers of, Jesus of Nazareth. This FAMILY fits the previous definition perfectly: as followers of Jesus, we are blood relatives. The blood Jesus shed for each one of us on that Roman cross is what makes us spiritual relatives.

Even the marriage part of the definition of FAMILY fits. As you read in your Bible, you will find out that all who BELIEVE in Jesus and accept Him as Rescuer and Lord, are collectively called His Bride. In the Bible, Jesus is referred to as the Bridegroom Who will one day return for His shining Bride, the group of BELIEVERS worldwide. And as a group of BELIEVERS, we are to treat one another with special loyalty and Godly intimacy (note the definition of FAMILY again).

We can CHOOSE to become part of God's FAMILY by accepting His Son and then joining a group of Bible BELIEVING Jesus followers — commonly called a church. (Note that the "church" is the people, not the building.) We have open access to authentic FAMILY interactions within a healthy church environment. It is like living in one big extended FAMILY — enjoying close relationships with babies, children, teens, young adults,

adults, and seniors too. (Many I know within our FAMILY of FAITH at Beaverton Christian Church feel closer connections to their spiritual FAMILY members, than to some of their own flesh and blood FAMILY members.)

 ## DO – Readers

DO realize that it is okay to begin looking for a FAMILY of FAITH even if you haven't yet made the CHOICE of FAITH in Jesus of Nazareth and the Bible. What better place to get a feel for what a church FAMILY might be like, than to slip in and observe one in action? It is not necessary to have any of the FAITH letters present in your life before you enter a church. If you have never experienced a FAMILY of FAITH for yourself, or if you've tried and the experience was less than satisfactory, I have some suggestions for your future explorations.

Hiking Boots and Churches

Make the CHOICE to begin looking for a good, strong, healthy FAMILY of FAITH. Be determined and patient in your search. This could take a while, but there can be adventure, discovery, and fun in the hunt. Take your time and visit many different places. There are mega-size, large, medium and small FAMILY groupings. See what size fits you the best. This process is kind of like making the purchase of a good pair of hiking boots. It is necessary that the boots are properly constructed, made to support your feet and keep them comfortable even under the harshest circumstances, and fit well. Let's run with this analogy.

Proper construction – Make sure that the Bible is the source of all teaching, with nothing added to it and nothing subtracted from it. A solid, reliable boot starts with a good last (a "last" is the shoemaker's model for shaping a shoe or boot). In my opinion, a good church is constructed on the solid, reliable last of the Bible.

Support and Comfort – A good pair of hiking boots should support your feet and keep them comfortable no matter where the trail leads. You may CHOOSE easy, well-marked urban hikes or take on the challenge of unmarked wilderness choose-your-own-adventure trails. You need to depend on the support and comfort of your boots especially when the trail is messy and rough. This is true of a good, strong, healthy FAMILY of FAITH, as well. In my opinion, a church worthy of the One in charge of it should be willing and able to give support and comfort to anyone willing to enter the door. Anyone. Especially if the trail of life has been messy and rough. If you find anything less, keep on looking. There are places just waiting for you to enter and find FAMILY.

A Good Fit – When you finally find the smooth, firm, properly constructed, support, and comfortable caress of a well-fitted boot, you know it. You know you've found the boots you need for the long haul. I suspect the same is true for a FAMILY of FAITH. On your way to finding a good fit you will almost certainly have many try-ons for proper construction and the necessary combo of support and comfort. This is a process — a process well worth the effort. In your search for a good fit some things to consider could be: your personal schedule and when the church you are visiting meets, the population represented in numbers, ages and diversity, and, of course, there has to be easy handicapped access to the buildings. When you find your good fit, I think you will know it.

Talking about hiking boots makes me want to tell you a true FAMILY story. I learned about hiking boots the hard way. Princess Pam made a grand, Grand Canyon mistake in the summer of 1963. Here's what happened.

Our family always had fun together no matter where we were and tent camping at the Canyon that summer was an extra bonus. Mom and Dad were 30-somethings, my kid brother was 10 and I was a very fashion conscious 15 year old Princess, in spite of the rustic conditions. People from all over the world came to experience the Grand Canyon and I planned to meet as many as possible. I knew I would impress whomever I would bump into with my winning personality and of course, the right apparel. In the summer of 1963, tight jeans, flimsy tops and white Keds were "in." Hiking boots (God forbid) were nowhere on the fashion chart. Of course, no socks were allowed with fashionably scuffed "whites." Only people from other countries and "old" people wore boots and socks.

They say that a person can't fully appreciate the Canyon without getting down inside it. Dad knew that was true and so he had an up-close-and-personal Canyon adventure in mind for my brother and me. (My mother was smart. She knew that while we were gone all day hiking in and out of the abyss, she could appreciate the Canyon just fine relaxing in the cool

Canyon ambiance of the Bright Angel Lodge.) Dad said he'd hike us down into the Canyon via the Bright Angel Trail to Indian Gardens. The park rangers warned that that particular hike would feel like four and a half miles going down the trail and like nine miles coming up and out. They had the notion that any hiker should carry a lot of water and wear a hat, a long sleeved shirt for sun protection, comfy pants, and of course good boots with appropriate socks. They stressed that one must be prepared for the rigors of the Trail. Now, while I did have a 15 year old sense of fashion, I had absolutely no sense of the physical challenges that awaited us.

Hiking the hot, dusty, manure laden switchbacks of the Bright Angel Trail in high summer is something for which one should be well prepared. Proper gear and enough water are essentials for survival. Dad told me to wear my "trail shoes" which would have provided better support and comfort for my tender feet. But no. I was sure to meet many someones on the trail and white Keds were a necessity. I simply had to look my best no matter the dire warnings of the park rangers and my Dad. My trail-wise father let me make my own CHOICE as to footwear for the hike. His decision to let me make a major mistake in judgment resulted in lifelong lessons. (Thank you, Dad.) Blind to the consequences that awaited me, this vain 15 year old girl smartly stepped onto the first switchback of the Bright Angel, blithely certain she could overcome any potential Trail trials. She possessed supreme confidence in her ability to overcome any physical adversity. She was wrong.

Early in the morning with the strong smell of hot pines, hot mule droppings, and hot Canyon dust, we started down. The Canyon was incredibly beautiful and majestic. Huge, yet intimate. And hot. Hiking downhill seemed relatively easy at first. My knees, ankles, and feet began "talking" to me around the second mile in. At approximately that point, I realized that a hat and better footwear would have been helpful. I was beginning to not care who I might meet or what I might look like. The trail was messy and rough. My lovely white Keds were already trashed. By the time we reached our destination of Indian Gardens, I was done in. My Dad and brother seemed fine. I was hot, hungry, thirsty, crabby, and in immense pain. Dad suggested that I take off my gritty, manure-crusted Keds and soak my blistered and bleeding feet in the cool stream that flowed through Indian Gardens. He encouraged me to try to relax, ignore the heat and pain and eat lunch with my feet sunk deep in the cool, soothing water. I tried, but I was scared. Every time I lifted my feet from the water, I could see the blisters oozing some kind of clear fluid and blood. I could feel every beat of my heart in my feet. I was a baby. I cried and blubbered. I knew I couldn't FACE the doubly demanding climb up and out of the Canyon. I was going to be a "drag out." A "drag out" was a person, just like me, who got into trouble in the Canyon and had to be hauled out on a mule. I begged my father to just leave me at Indian Gardens and send a mule. He said, number one, the fee for such an extraction was extravagant, and number two, I could make it out on my own two feet. I knew I couldn't. I'd hit the wall. He knew I could.

Dad was in prolonged and active combat during World War II. He served in the armored infantry. He was quite familiar with battered feet. He calmly told me to take my feet out of the water, let them air dry, and put my Keds back on, bleeding blisters and all. I sobbed at the thought, but he insisted. He assured me that if I would listen to him and do as he said, I would make it out. Scared and in pain, I believed him. He told me that at first my feet would hurt like crazy, but after about 10 minutes of hiking, all the flapping, bruised and bleeding skin would wear off inside those Keds, and the pain would fade away, until later. I trusted what he said. He was right.

It was a difficult ascent in intense heat. My compassionate brother carried my canteen for me. (He also allowed numerous thirsty strangers to drink from it as he preceded his hobbling sister up the trail. Yuck. But by then, I didn't care whose saliva I shared.) Hours later, (I don't remember how many. I think I've repressed that memory.) we finally reached the top of Bright Angel and the south rim of the Canyon. With Dad's wisdom and encouragement I had not become another "drag out." Mom greeted us with joy and praise for our accomplishment. I just felt dizzy and sick.

When we reached our tent I collapsed onto my sleeping bag and tore off those Keds. Then, once again, the pain began in earnest. Mom, using her best first aid techniques, tried to soothe my oozing, throbbing feet. Nothing worked. Not the aspirin, not the cold compresses, not the salve, not the bandages. Nothing worked. Pain was my lot. I had not heeded the warnings and I was paying big time consequences for my vanity. There was one more consequence to bear.

Even after the sun went down and I'd had a little supper to eat, I still felt spent and dizzy and sick. I was almost certainly suffering from heat exhaustion since I had a low grade fever complete with sweats and then chills. My family was caring for me well and the only place I had to walk was the closest campground "wash-house." Beyond embarrassment, I leaned on my mother and completed my last painful trek to the wash-house before sack time. I took up my sleeping position in the tent.

The tent — now, that's a memory ripe in my mind, to this day. It was a heavy canvas umbrella tent with a center pole. I remember the hot canvas smell giving way to a cool canvas smell as I lay in agony on top of my too-hot-for-the-Canyon sleeping bag. But as the air cooled with the night, I managed to get my mangled feet and aching body inside my bag. When I said "sleeping position" in the previous paragraph, I meant it. Each member of my family had assigned sleeping positions in the tent. Dad had it planned this way for optimal use of the limited space within the tent. When you faced the thing and the huge metal zipper that opened and closed it, our positions were as follows: Dad on the far left, Mom next to Dad and the center pole, my brother next to Mom and the center pole, and me on the far right. There was no room to spare. When we zipped up that tent at night, we were like four mummies laid out in perfect symmetry and close proximity. Are you getting the picture?

Sometime in the early morning darkness, when everyone else was deep in blissful slumber, I had to throw up. We were all so closely packed together on the floor of the tent that all I had to do was turn my face in my mom's direction and I was breathing my brother's breath. We were that close. I turned in Mom's direction and quietly moaned, "Mom, I have to throw up." ... Blissful slumber turned into quick and purposeful actions. My kid brother unzipped his bag and the tent flap in record time; Mom unzipped her bag and somehow found a cooking pot stored on the campsite table; and I somehow got my head far enough outside the tent flap to hit the cooking pot. (Just remembering this incident now, makes me feel like barfing.) I can't remember what Dad did. I just know that I felt a bit better after all the action, and was able, with the others to finally sleep until daylight.

Needless to say, I suffered many days of pain and discomfort because of my poor CHOICE of hiking footwear. When we arrived home after our Canyon vacation, Dad was gracious enough to have me fitted for a good pair of hiking boots. I gratefully accepted his offer. After many stores and many try-ons, I decided on an excellent pair of hand made boots from Italy. He bought me several pairs of hiking socks as well. Those boots took me comfortably on many other family vacations and hikes with never *a blister in sight. Thanks, Dad, I love you. And you too, Mom. And you too, my canteen-sharing kid brother. I love you all. Lessons learned — trust my Dad and follow his advice. Never let my brother carry my canteen again. The Grand Canyon is always beautiful and awesome — even when you are vain and in pain. Get a good pair of hiking boots and wear them — with socks. FAMILY is essential to survival.*

 ## DO – Readers

DO know too, that even if you have super-support and love from your own genetic FAMILY, as I do, the plus of a church FAMILY is an extra-added bonus that is irreplaceable. It is an incredibly beautiful thing to have spiritual children, grandchildren, sisters, brothers, grandmas, grandpas, etc. The close bonds of our blood relationship through Jesus are unbreakable and I rely on these bonds of relationship every day of my life: through prayer support, phone calls, rides to the store and the doctor, etc. And through these bonds of love, I can serve others in ways that are unique. This service to others is important to their well being and mine as well. You can enjoy the FAMILY of the children of God, too. If you are not already involved in a FAMILY of FAITH, DO find a good church and get involved!

DO know too, that there are no perfect church FAMILIES, and no perfect followers of Jesus, just as there are no perfect genetically related FAMILIES. There always seems to be a crazy Uncle Albert somewhere, a grumpy Grandma Louise, and a bratty little cousin Cory! (Insert your own choice of names if you want.) In my opinion, if you've found "the perfect church," somebody is being perfectly phony. I think it's fun to have to learn to get along with others and help them learn to get along with me. I am, in no way, perfect. I'll admit it. Quite the admission for a Princess.

Even though I am blessed with a close and loving, genetically related FAMILY, I know I need to be part of the FAMILY of God. Especially as a handicapper, I need to be able to count on the love, acceptance, assistance, biblical teaching, wisdom, humor, and prayers of my spiritual FAMILY at Beaverton Christian Church. There are so many I love, and so many that love me back. (Even on the frequent occasions when I goof up.) I also, especially as a handicapper, need to be of service. And my

> *FAMILY at BCC gives me ample opportunity to serve in many ways. I wouldn't be complete without my church FAMILY to love, hug, and laugh with, to cry with, rejoice with, mourn with, pray with, and eat with — to simply be with. That's the honest truth. How I love the FAMILY of God! Thanks, you all.*

DO you enjoy close, healthy relationships with your genetic family? DO you belong to the FAMILY of God? DO you have a church home? Are you an active member of this FAMILY? Are you loving and serving others? Are you learning more and more of God's Word, the Bible? DO you pray with and for others? DO you enjoy close, loving relationships with anyone? Please DO write below about your relationships or non-relationships within your genetic FAMILY and the FAMILY of God. Is FAMILY important to you? Would you like to be a member of the FAMILY of God?

I've asked a lot of questions. Here is a big box to write in. Please write. This will help you sort through some FAMILY issues.

 **DON'T – Readers**

DON'T turn your back on your FAMILY members, whether they are biological, legal or spiritual members, because of pride, stubbornness, or those dreaded feelings of dependency. (It's OK to lean on others. It has to be. I have to. Maybe you do too, as either the handicapper or the care-giver.)

DON'T give in to feelings of uselessness. No matter what you are FACING, there are ways to contribute to your FAMILY, unless you are literally in a coma. I mean it! Search for ways to be of service to others. You not only help them, you get a boost from your efforts.

Write down some ways you can help out your FAMILY, either genetic or spiritual. (Hopefully both.) Can you help them out even a little bit every day? This not only helps them, it helps you. Think and write.

Listen to what the writer of the book of Hebrews writes to the church he cared for, in Hebrews 10:24-25. "And let us consider how we may spur one another on toward love and good deeds. Let us not give up meeting together, as some are in the habit of doing, but let us encourage one another — and all the more as you see the Day approaching" True! It is vitally important for followers of Jesus to regularly meet together for mutual FAMILY talks, fun, Bible study, meals, celebrations, and support as we eagerly await the "Day" of Jesus' return for His Bride: the world-wide FAMILY of FAITH.

One of my favorite Bible teachers at our church (the one who calls me Yoda and is now a pastor of a church in California) used to stress the importance of meeting together regularly by saying, "Lone rangers get picked off." How can we get picked off, you ask? We can get picked off by the enemy of our souls and his dark cohorts, the world that surrounds us, and our own selfish little selves. We all need to be active members of a FAMILY of FAITH: for God, for the FAMILY and for ourselves. Don't be a lone ranger. "Don't give up meeting together." The key word here, is DON'T.

I'll keep this one short. I'm not a good lone ranger. "Don't give up meeting together," is an easy one for me. I know that when I meet with my church FAMILY, I am going to be energized, enlivened, and enclosed with arms of love. I know I do the same for others, as we meet together. It is so cool. I DON'T want to get "picked off". I CHOOSE to be an active member of my Beaverton Christian FAMILY. DON'T you get picked off! Meet regularly and often. God's FAMILY is fun!

What are some CHOICES you can make concerning your genetic and/or spiritual FAMILY connections? Is it easy for you to connect or is it an effort? What are some benefits that would make connecting worth the effort?

I DARE both you cappers and caregivers to get deeply involved in FAMILY — in your genetic grouping if possible, and for sure, in the FAMILY of FAITH, a healthy Bible-teaching church. Participate as fully as you can. If you are already deeply involved, wonderful. If you have great genetic connections and a caring FAMILY, as I do, enjoy their love, and care and communications to the fullest. Be there for them too, as an active participant in their lives (as active as you can be under your FACING IT circumstances). Are you deeply involved in FAMILY? Name some FAMILY members you regularly interact with. Do you need to work on more participation?

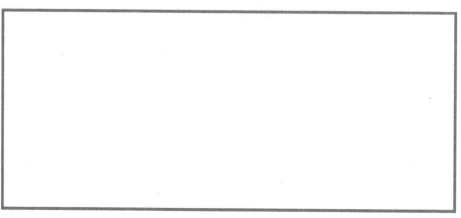

If you are a capper or caregiver without great or even good, genetic FAMILY support and interactions, I DARE you to find your very own FAITH FAMILY. This is a FAMILY you get to CHOOSE. CHOOSE well and enjoy an incredible depth of varied relationships with the followers of Jesus of Nazareth!

If you're still on the fence when it comes to this Jesus of Nazareth, then I want to extend this DARE to you in a special way. DARE to get involved in a FAMILY of FAITH to the extent that you can. Start your hunt for a church. (Remember the hiking boots.) Let people know where you stand. Begin to participate in church activities and you will begin to build relationships with those who are members of this FAMILY of FAITH. I DARE you to take the time to find a place to do this.

How do you feel about this DARE?

Caregivers and Handicappers

Will you please reflect, think, pray, and ADAPT concerning this area of interactions with FAMILY? How can you make sure you spend time with them? How can you help them? How can they help you? Do you need to restore particular relationships? There are so many ways you can ADAPT to the CHOICE of connecting with FAMILY. Please write your thoughts, ideas, and reactions.

You are now ready to record daily any interactions you may have with your FAMILY: genetic or spiritual. Plan and record visits, calls, e-mails, trips to the store, celebrations ... whatever. Plan it. Do it. Record it. Enjoy your FAMILY!

Now on to the 3rd F of our 4 good CHOICES: FRIENDS.

216

Chapter 8

The 4 Fs of Choice:

FRIENDS

FRIEND – Definition: A person whom one knows and with whom one has a bond of mutual affection, typically exclusive of sexual or family relations.

FRIENDS. Who doesn't want FRIENDS? To have one or two good FRIENDS is to be rich, in my opinion. How would you describe a good FRIEND? Go ahead, both handicapper and caregiver, and write down what you consider characteristics of a good FRIEND. See if you can come up with at least five traits of a good FRIEND.

As I think of what it means to me to have a good FRIEND, I think of words like: love, joy, peace, patience, kindness, goodness, faithfulness, gentleness, and self-control. (As a Type I diabetic, I really need a good FRIEND to help me with self-control. I love chocolate.) In my lifetime I have been blessed with good FRIENDS. (I say lifetime, and I mean it. It takes time, and lots of it, to develop and grow a good FRIENDSHIP. That's a whole other book, or maybe I'll get to just talk about it.) I am ever thankful to my Lord, Who brought dear FRIENDS into my life. I am ever thankful to each of them, who have so enriched my life with their FRIENDSHIP and who allow me to enrich theirs. Some live close and some live far away and some are already waiting for me in Heaven. All are precious to me. And all these FRIENDS somehow continue to let me be the Princess, and they seem to enjoy the experience as much as I do. True FRIENDS.

Handicappers and caregivers — please write in the box the names of your FRIENDS. If you have none to write yet, don't despair! There's help coming in this section on FRIENDS.

DO – Readers

DO keep your eyes open (or in my case, eye open) for FRIENDS whenever you have contact with other people. Always be on the lookout for potential FRIENDS. Always. Everywhere. DO meet peoples' eyes with your own. Give them a smile. This is a pleasant surprise for many a stranger. Always be aware of other people wherever you find yourself: a waiting room at the doctor's office, sitting at the bus stop, on the bus, shopping, at the gym (if you can make it there), at work, at the rehab center, at church, in your neighborhood. You get my drift. You never know when your smile or a simple hello could open the door to the beginning of a lifelong FRIENDSHIP. This is equally important for cappers and caregivers.

February 12, 1996. It was a clear, cold, windy morning in Portland, Oregon. I was still "normal" and out for a solitary walk in our new neighborhood. We had moved to the blue house on the hill the previous October. I was lonely. I needed a FRIEND. Close by. A FRIEND within walking distance.

The home we had moved from had been in a cul-de-sac and we had lived there for ten years. I'd been surrounded by close neighbors and had a good FRIEND right across the street. She and I would see each other almost every day and touch base with each other. Her daughter was (and still is) like a fourth daughter to us. Even though we still got together often after our move, it wasn't the same. I missed her and our daily, easy access to each other.

Back to February 12, 1996 and my brisk morning walk in our hilly new neighborhood. I was enjoying the cold wind as I hiked the hills and explored new ways to get my mile workout. Ever since we'd moved I'd been asking God to please give me a new FRIEND in this new part of town. Four months had gone by. When what to my wandering eyes should appear (I still had two functional ones then), but a woman walking in my direction on the other side of the street. She was alone too. As we approached each other I could tell she was quite pregnant, even though she was wrapped in a big warm coat. Still keeping up my walking speed, I smiled and hollered across the street, "Hi! When's your baby due?" She smiled back at me, hollered a return greeting, and told me her due date. We both kept on walking right past each other and around different corners.

After I rounded the corner, I began to realize I had just missed a great opportunity to actually meet this young woman. I could have — I should have — slowed my pace, crossed the stupid street and talked a bit with her. Good grief. For an extrovert, I gave myself a failing grade and suffered the regret of a blown opportunity to actually talk with a woman who must certainly live close by. (After all, she was on foot, it was very cold and she was very pregnant.) Way to go Princess Pam.

I kept on walking as I beat myself up. When I reached my home street and strode down the steep hill towards our little blue house, I was given a second chance. Wow. Here she came again. Walking up the hill towards me. Yippee! I knew what to do this time. I greeted her face-to-face and standing at a slant on our hill, we talked with each other. We were getting cold just standing there, so I invited her in for a hot cup of herbal tea. She accepted the invitation.

That began a deep FRIENDSHIP that continues to this day. She lived about 10 houses down our hill on the very same street. And get this: she had been praying for a FRIEND too. We call each other on our anniversary and try to get together every February 12th. We both clearly remember our double-chance first meeting and we have special fun celebrating that particular date. How I love her. And I almost blew my opportunity to get to know her. Whew! I have learned over the years to be keenly aware of those around me. I never know who just might be looking for a good FRIEND.

You never know just whom you might meet in the course of your every day life, either — any old time, any old where. So, DO keep your eyes open and be ready to greet your next new FRIEND. Are you willing to DO this DO? Where are some places you just might bump into a new FRIEND? Go ahead and write.

 DON'T – Readers

DON'T be like Princess Pam on her power walk through the new neighborhood — so centered on self that I would have missed one of my best FRIENDS of all time if we hadn't been given that second-chance meeting on the morning of February 12, 1996. My life would not be as rich as it is if I hadn't been given that second chance. Please DON'T close your eyes to those around you, wherever you may be. Sometimes there aren't second chances. (I'm talking to myself here, too.) Please write down a time you passed up an opportunity to get to know someone. What were the circumstances? And what will you do in the future so you don't pass up another opportunity?

 DARE – Readers

This is going to be a very specific DARE. I DARE you to be on the lookout for potential FRIENDS for one week, starting now. Pay close attention to the people you encounter in your daily routines for just one week. For extroverts, this is a fun DARE, but for introverts, I realize this could be an annoying DARE. But it just doesn't matter, because I *am* the Princess and I am DARING you. Just for a week, open your eyes, be aware of others and smile and interact. In order to have a FRIEND, you have to first meet one. (Of course, I'm assuming you use your brains and make certain your interactions are *safe*.) So I DARE you. Are you ready to accept this mission? Get creative in the following box and track yourself and your people interactions for one week. What are the results? Handicappers, do you need help to get out to more people places? Caregivers, how can you help your capper? Did you meet someone new during this DARING week? Write about your experiences.

DO – Readers

DO spend time with your FRIENDS. This seems like a no-brainer, but it really isn't. Time spent together is what builds FRIENDSHIPS. Time together is absolutely essential to the health and life of a FRIENDSHIP, and FRIENDSHIP is absolutely essential to the health and life of both handicappers and caregivers. You can enjoy time together on the phone, at your home, at their home, e-mailing, text-messaging, shopping, going out to eat, at the gym, during Bible study, praying together. Share your joys and your griefs with one another. I know you know what I'm talking about. DO take time out with FRIENDS or the health and life of your FRIENDSHIP will suffer. How can you follow through on this DO this week?

DON'T – Readers

DON'T neglect your FRIENDS. It's as simple as that. Are you neglecting to put in the time it takes to maintain healthy FRIENDSHIPS? DON'T let physical disabilities keep you away from your FRIENDS. If you are neglecting your FRIENDS, what is getting in your way?

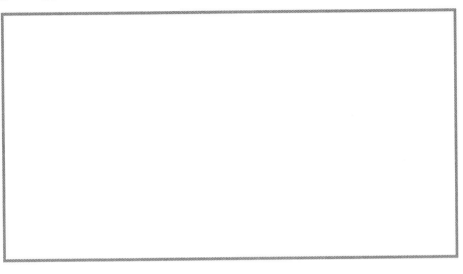

 DARE – Readers

This is a specific DARE, too. I DARE you to commit to interacting with at least one FRIEND every day for the rest of your life. You heard me. Every day for the rest of your life, starting now. You can keep track of these FRIENDLY interactions daily, in your *Facing It Journal*. The DARE is on. Plan it. Do it. Record it. The CHOICE is yours. If you drop the ball and miss a few days, start bouncing it again and contact a FRIEND. Keep up this so-important contact and keep on journaling. This DARE is for your benefit. How do you feel about this for-the-rest-of-your-life DARE?

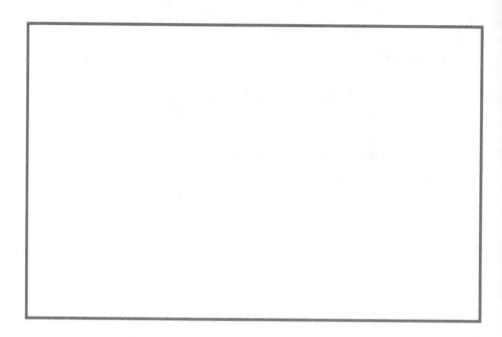

If at this point in your life you have no one you call FRIEND, you now have some ways to begin to find such a person. If you enjoy the companionship of FRIENDS then you can now make sure you continue to enrich and grow your FRIENDSHIPS. Journal, and keep on journaling, my FRIENDS! No matter your personal situation, some really good news about FRIENDSHIP is coming up next.

By now, you shouldn't be surprised when I tell you that Jesus of Nazareth is the Main Character in this third good F of FRIENDS. This is really good news, whether you have 10 good FRIENDS or none at all, because Jesus is the one and only perfect FRIEND, regardless of circumstances. Jesus spoke these words to His followers while He was still on earth. Jesus' good FRIEND, John, (the John who wrote the gospel of John, which I really want you to read) recorded his FRIEND'S words to them (and to us) in John 15:13-15 — "Greater love has no one than this, that he lay down his life for his friends. You are my friends if you do what I command. I no longer call you servants, because a servant does not know his master's business. Instead, I have called you friends, for everything that I learned from my Father I have made known to you."

This is pretty clear. Jesus tells His listeners that He CHOOSES to be their FRIEND. And He CHOOSES to be a FRIEND today, to all who BELIEVE and willingly follow His commands. The next CHOICE is up to us. We have the opportunity to CHOOSE Jesus as our FRIEND. Not only is He the Risen Savior, Good Shepherd, Forgiver, Lord, King, Creator, the Living Word, the First and the Last, and the Bright Morning Star, but He also calls Himself our FRIEND.

God Talked Back

The first time I heard God talk back to me I was alone in the car, driving. I was desperate and pleading out loud. All that came out of my mouth was, "Please don't let her nose bleed. Please don't let her nose bleed. Please don't let her nose bleed." Here's the story.

It was a hot, sunny, day in Portland, Oregon. (Yes, it can happen.) A special day in many ways. It was the bat mitzvah day for a good FRIEND of our middle daughter. (Bat mitzvah – Definition: a religious initiation ceremony for a Jewish girl aged twelve years and one day, regarded as the age of religious maturity; the girl undergoing such a ceremony; from the Hebrew, meaning "daughter of the commandment.) This was also a big day for our own daughter who had just turned thirteen. She was happy for her FRIEND and looking forward to being in a synagogue for the first time. She was looking forward to witnessing her

227

FRIEND complete what was required during the traditional ceremony. And, with just a little anxiety that enhanced the excitement, she was looking forward to attending the big celebration that was to follow her FRIEND's bat mitzvah. She would be attending a formal sit-down dinner that included family and friends of the daughter of the commandment and after the formalities, there was going to be a bust loose, have fun, huge party that would include a deejay and dancing. This would be our daughter's first boy/girl dance. She had a new white dress hanging in her closet, ready to wear to the festivities. A special day was in the making.

Early that morning the nose bleeds began. Ever since she'd been a little girl, when the weather was hot and dry, she was subject to nose bleeds. Big, bloody, hard to control nose bleeds. The kind that laid her on her back with an icepack on her nose. She'd suffered several that morning of the bat mitzvah. And both of us were worried. What if? What if? What if it began to bleed at some critical moment in the synagogue ceremony? What if her nose chose to spurt during the fancy sit-down food and cake time? What if (God forbid) she was dancing with some boy and her nose decided to gush. What if?

It was time to go. I drove our girl to the appointed place and dropped her off. She looked fresh and young and beautiful in her fitted white dress as she waved goodbye. I loved her so much. I so wanted her to enjoy this day. As I drove away, I was afraid. Her nose might bleed again. She was wearing white. White! The humiliation of a nose bleed would be horrendous. She needed help. I needed help. And the two big handkerchiefs she was packing (just in case) wouldn't be enough. The only One I could think of that might be able to help, was God. So, on my drive home I began begging. At that point in time I had only one request. "Please don't let her nose bleed. Please don't let her nose bleed. Please don't let her nose bleed." Over and over and over and over I begged while trying to safely make it home. I poured all of my heart into those six words. Over and over and over and over, repeating the cry of my heart.

At the beginning of this story, I told you that this was a special day in many ways. It was. It was a special day for the bat mitzvah FRIEND and her family, for our daughter, and for me. Yes, for me as well. This was the first day of my life that I cried out to God and heard Him answer back. I heard the voice of God. You heard me right. I heard the very voice of God, for the very first time, that bat mitzvah day.

As I continued to repeat those impassioned six words, alone in my car, I was suddenly cut off in mid plea. "Enough, already!" Enough, already? He sounded like a Jewish father a bit put out with his child's constant pestering. His answer was surprising, funny, and enough. I was immediately put at ease. The implication behind His answer to me was that He was in charge and all would be well. Why should I be worried? I'd just heard God talk back. In fact, He'd interrupted me. "Enough, already!"

As I drove on I was amazed at what I'd just experienced. It was more than just the words I'd heard. Somehow God had opened to me a new understanding of Who He was when He said, "Enough, already!" He showed me in those two words that He was actively involved in my life and my daughter's life. He revealed something new to me about His character. He cared about nose bleeds and first boy/girl parties and a mother's worries. When He spoke to me He was emphatic, dramatic, and comical. He was commanding and compassionate, strong and gentle, stern and loving, imperative and intimate, teasing, but not hurtful. It was an unexpected, delightful encounter for me. I guess I really didn't even realize I was "praying." I was simply pouring out my heart to Him six words at a time. And He talked back. Wow.

That was the first time I realized I had an Ally and a FRIEND I could always talk with. I had a FRIEND willing and ready to listen and answer back no matter what I brought to Him. I could fill the rest of this book with amazing, true stories of answered prayers and the accompanying revelations of God's character that continue to transform my life as I learn to believe Him, trust Him and remain loyal to Him. He is my best FRIEND. I talk with Him every day and He talks back.

Needless to say, when Jim and I picked our daughter up later that evening, she was fine. More than fine. She had enjoyed a wonderful bat mitzvah celebration and never once needed a hankie. All was well. Enough, already.

What do you think about this? As a handicapper? As a caregiver? Is being FRIENDS with Jesus a new idea to you or have you been FRIENDS for ages? Think about the opportunity of being FRIENDS with Jesus. Maybe you speak with Him daily, and maybe you have never entertained such an idea. What would you like to say to Him right now? He's listening even as you write. Be ready to receive a reply.

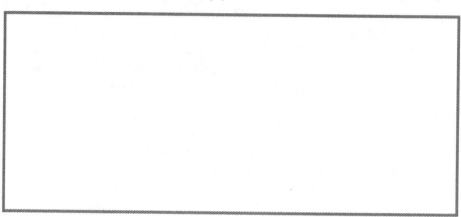

 DO – Readers

Please DO read the book of John in your *Zondervan NIV Study Bible*, or your *NIV Quest Study Bible*. Read it, whether or not you're already a follower of Jesus. Read it again, if you've already read it, or read it for the first time, and see how Jesus was FRIEND to John and the others. John knew that he was a dearly loved FRIEND of Jesus. You will be reading his eyewitness account of the life of Jesus, His FRIEND. DO know that Jesus is willing and eager to be **your** very best FRIEND. This relationship of best FRIEND is open to anyone willing to name Him Rescuer and Lord and follow His commands. DO take the time that is required of any good FRIENDSHIP, and invest in the relationship of a lifetime. DO pick up your Bible and learn Who it is that desires FRIENDSHIP with you. Please accept His offer and enjoy the very best of FRIENDS, now and forever. Please DO!

Scavenger Hunts and Treasures

I've asked you to read the Gospel of John. So, what's in it for you? Fun. Adventure. Excitement. Treasures. FRIENDSHIP. If, and I say if, you open and read, asking God to talk to you, seeking Who He is and what He has to say, and if you're willing to knock, knock, knock and wait for Him to answer the door — fun, adventure, excitement, treasures and FRIENDSHIP await. Jesus said, "Ask and it will be given to you; seek and you will find; knock and it will be opened to you. For everyone who asks receives; he who seeks finds; and to him who knocks, the door will be opened." (Mathew 7:7&8) Cool. When we read our Bibles in this way I think it's kind of like the ultimate scavenger hunt.

> *Have you ever been on a scavenger hunt? I think I've been on a least a million. They were the rage when I was a ten year old kid in the late 1950s. (Scavenger hunt – Definition: a game, typically played in an extensive outdoor area, in which participants have to collect a number of miscellaneous objects.) That definition is okay, but it doesn't convey the fun (and often funny) creative genius of a bunch of neighborhood kids (boys and girls played this game together) writing down the treasures to be sought on an "official" list, the thrill of the hunt, the excitement of a time limit, the freedom of running the neighborhood streets, the wild banging on door after door as we sought the treasured items, the hope that the occupants would hurry to their door and give us what we asked for, the hasty but polite asking for a necessary item on the list, the joy of adding yet another required scavenged object to the bag, or the feeling of accomplishment as all who played the game assembled and the various groups of kids counted out the number of items they'd managed to collect.*
>
> *Who would win? Would any team bag everything on the list? The fun was in the hunt. The adventure was running free with two or three teammates. The excitement was knocking on a door with sweaty fists and hoping that the occupants would open up and give us the game winning item. And the treasures, of course, were all the various listed objects we could dump out of our bag at the agreed rendezvous. It was so satisfying to pour out the contents of a full sack.*
>
> *We were like gold miners panning for nuggets as we stepped up to each door and asked for gold. Back in those days, the gold to be collected in the team bag could include a clothes pin, a red crayon, a cancelled stamp, a safety pin, a bottle cap, a blue rubber band, a piece of hard candy, a cat's-eye marble, a page of the Sunday comics, a bobby pin, a band aid, a penny, a green balloon, a postcard, a popsicle stick; whatever the teams decided that day's gold would be. A scavenger hunt spelled fun, adventure, excitement and treasures for all participants from beginning to end.*

I invite you to read the book of John with an excited, scavenger hunt mentality. Are you willing to ask, seek, knock and find? Do you want God to open His door and give you some treasure? He will talk with you through His Word, FRIEND to FRIEND. Do you want to hear His voice?

Are you willing to ask? Are you willing to seek? Are you willing to knock? Do you want to find? Every time I open the Gospel of John (or any other part of the Bible) with an ask, seek and knock attitude, I find out something new that God wants me to know. Every time. You will too. That's treasure.

Will you DO this DO? Are you interested in a new FRIENDSHIP with Jesus? Are you interested in a better FRIENDSHIP with Jesus? DO read the Gospel of John and take note of Who this Jesus is. There is space here to write down what strikes you about Him as you read. Is He Someone you could trust to be your FRIEND? What is HE saying to you as you read? Did you find any gold?

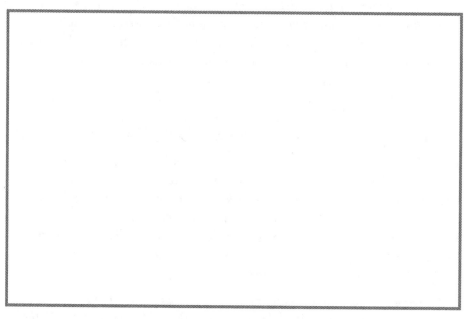

 DON'T – Readers

Please DON'T turn your back to the best FRIEND you could **ever** have. Don't leave your study Bible on the shelf. Pick it up. Open it up. Don't neglect the words recorded by John, whom Jesus considered a good FRIEND. Whether you are currently FACING IT alone, or with good FRIENDS surrounding you, you need Jesus to be your ultimate best FRIEND. If this handicapped Princess needs His FRIENDSHIP, you do too, cappers. If my Prince Charming of a caregiver husband needs His

FRIENDSHIP, you do too, caregivers. Every person on the face of the earth needs His FRIENDSHIP. He is always available. He is never too busy, never too tired, never self-centered. He will never abandon you or let you down. Never. He is all-powerful and your only Protector from the enemy of your soul. He always knows what is best for you and always pursues that course for you. He wants intimate, Godly, FRIENDSHIP with you, and with me. DON'T turn away from the most perfect FRIENDSHIP ever offered you. Please DON'T. In that turning away, you hurt Him and yourself and those around you. I know. I once CHOSE to turn down His FRIENDSHIP. For 15 years.

Oh yeah. Fifteen years of going it alone without my perfect best FRIEND. My CHOICE. An uninformed, stubborn, prideful, hurtful, harmful, self-centered, self-defeating, CHOICE to turn away from the One Who continued to daily offer me His hand and heart in FRIENDSHIP. Here's what happened.

We had just moved to Portland, Oregon, from Southern California, in the winter of 1976. (That was quite the adjustment. We quickly learned that umbrellas were a dead give-away that we were foreigners and threw them in the back of the closet. True Oregonians just function in rain, like Californians function in sunshine. It's only water, after all.)

Our oldest daughter was 4 years old and I was pregnant with our second daughter. (Our third daughter was still hiding out, getting ready for a surprise entrance into our family, only 15 months after her preceding sister. She was a delightful, if unexpected, surprise. But I'm getting sidetracked, like any mama will, thinking about her babies ... back to the story at hand.) Jim and I had just started attending a church in our neighborhood that had a good, Bible-based reputation. We'd only attended there for about four Sundays in a row when "it" happened.

Our sweet, darling, 4 year old daughter, came out of her Sunday school class, crying. When our little girl was able to control her sobs, she told us the WHY of her crocodile tears. Her Sunday school teacher had asked the group of four year olds, what songs they'd like to sing that morning. Our girl promptly answered with one of her favorite country tunes that her grandma liked to sing. The insensitive woman (Can you tell I still have strong feelings about her?) proceeded to embarrass and humiliate our girl in front of the class. She told our daughter, and the class, that her choice was "a bad song," and had no place in church. The teacher harshly upbraided a totally innocent, four year old girl's response to her question. I was furious! Jim wasn't happy. Our daughter was upset and confused by this woman's response to one of her favorite songs. (I don't blame her.) Monday, I called the church and let them know what had happened and that they would never see us there again! Indeed, we never went back to that particular church. Ever. (It seems now, that everyone involved, over-reacted, but that was then.)

I so over-reacted, that I let one woman's inappropriate response, drive me away from not only that particular church, but from Jesus, Himself. In my mind, I equated Him with that Sunday school teacher and her hurtful actions. I didn't know any better; because I had never taken the time to develop FRIENDSHIP with the One I still only knew as Rescuer. I hadn't yet, in my life, submitted to His Lordship. How could I? I didn't know Him, because I didn't know what He had to say to me about Himself. I had spent very little time in my Bible. So in my magnificent wisdom, I let one woman's actions poison my view of Who Jesus is, and for 15, count 'em, 15 years, I remained in that estranged state. In my outrage, stubbornness, and ignorance, I built up a wall of spiritual self-sufficiency that kept out the best of all FRIENDS, Jesus.

It was only when I responded to a good FRIEND's invitation to go with her and her husband to Beaverton Christian Church that I finally started on the path to FRIENDSHIP with Jesus. (Thanks, Peggy!) The Palm Sunday I told you about in the WHO AM I? Section, was when I began to understand that spiritual self-sufficiency has no place in the life of a follower and FRIEND of Jesus. He makes it clear in John 15:13-15, that we are His FRIENDS if, if, **if**, we DO what He commands. DO what He commands? How can we know what He commands? We can know what He commands, if we read and understand His Book, the Bible. WHY should we want to do that? So we can enjoy FRIENDSHIP with Him.

I was an idiot. I know that now. I know what it is like to live without Jesus as Lord and FRIEND. (I will never CHOOSE that course again.) Now I know the difference between people who are followers of Jesus, and Jesus Himself. He is perfect. None of His followers are. I judged Him, when I judged that Sunday school teacher's actions. I now know that she acted inappropriately, I acted inappropriately, and Jesus remained, as always, perfect. Patient. Pure. And faithful to me, even when I wasn't faithful to Him. I have forgiven her (it's true) and He has forgiven me. Whew!

The most valuable lesson I learned was to never equate Jesus, Who is God, with His followers, who are flawed, imperfect human beings, who daily need His guidance and forgiveness and FRIENDSHIP. I turned my back on Him, because of a person's words and actions. I will not make that mistake again. His FRIENDSHIP is just too valuable. I CHOOSE to make Him Lord and learn to follow His commands. Please DON'T make the same mistakes I made. Learn from my ignorance, and CHOOSE Jesus as your very best FRIEND, for now, and for always.

Has anything like this ever happened to you? What do you want to write?

 DARE – Readers

Here comes the DARE. Will you DARE to share a mutual bond of affection with Jesus of Nazareth? Will you DARE to get to know Him and let Him get to know you? Will you DARE to look into your study Bible and read the book that John wrote about his best FRIEND? Will you DARE to study the Bible as a whole; to get a full, accurate picture of the One Who is willing to be your very best FRIEND? Will you DARE to put in the work that a good FRIENDSHIP requires? Shared time together, honest, open communication, listening, getting to know your FRIEND better and better over the years? FRIENDSHIP with Jesus is the best FRIENDSHIP you will ever experience.

Some ways I join Him in mutual affection are in prayer (talking, thinking, pondering, listening), Bible study, and praise and worship. We have a variety of CDs that help me come closer to my FRIEND in music and song. (I have no rhythm, and a tin ear with a voice to match, but He doesn't care. He's my FRIEND.)

Please DARE to join Him in the bonds of mutual affection. Will you DARE? What are some ways you could become a closer FRIEND with Jesus?

Caregivers and Handicappers

Once again, I'm asking you to reflect, think, pray, and ADAPT concerning this CHOICE of FRIENDS. Please write your thoughts, ideas, and reactions.

Using your *Facing It Journal* you are now ready to record daily the interactions you may have with your FRIENDS. You might also record how you are seeking new FRIENDSHIPS each day. And be sure to touch base with Jesus as FRIEND at least once a day as you pray and read your Bible. Enjoy your FRIENDS!

In my opinion, touching base with God every day is of utmost importance and absolutely essential. I need to know our FRIENDSHIP is strong because I don't know what challenges I may have to FACE on any given day. I need to know the close touch of my Ally and FRIEND. And the best way I can know Him close and near is in prayer and Bible reading. I consider daily prayer and Bible reading so essential that each is listed at the top of the *Facing It Journal* page with a check off box for each. Plan it. Do it. Check it off. Every day.

I always begin my day by praying the Lord's Prayer, praying personal, conversational prayers, and reading the Bible. I CHOOSE to mark a beautiful X in each of those essential three page topping boxes every day. It's a good CHOICE for me. I CHOOSE to start every day of my life conversing with my best FRIEND. Talking and listening. How does this work? I'll explain.

Each morning I awake with the Lord's Prayer as my starter. While still in bed, in the quiet of the morning, I pray the way my FRIEND taught His FRIENDS to pray. Jesus said, "This, then, is how you should pray: 'Our Father in heaven, hallowed be your name, your kingdom come, your will be done, on earth as it is in heaven. Give us today our daily bread. Forgive us our debts as we also have forgiven our debtors. And lead us not into temptation, but deliver us from the evil one.'" (Matthew 6:9-13) This is not rote for me. I pray this model prayer of Jesus personally and passionately, considering every word. If I catch myself simply repeating the familiar words without considering each one a precious gem, I begin again and pray in earnest. It is a complete and meaningful prayer that prepares me for each day.

Then I move on to my own personal, conversational prayers that usually revolve around FAMILY and FRIENDS, but often include situations and people in the news and around the world. Depending on the particular morning, my best FRIEND may listen to me ask Him for help for me or for others, ask Him for wisdom to make a decision, tell Him what I think should happen next, thank Him for some particular, beg Him for another — my communications with Him can go all over the board. Then I wait for Him to answer back and let me know His will. (That's the hard part — waiting for His answer and then graciously accepting His will, especially if it differs from mine.) Over the years He has answered me in many different ways and not necessarily according to my time schedule or my desires. But He has always answered in some way, and I trust that this FRIEND knows best. I have received answers to prayer from Him verbally (like the bat mitzvah nose bleed episode) several times. Each of those audible responses is quite memorable in its own way. He has spoken to me in dreams, visions, and specific circumstances that only He could orchestrate. It has taken time to learn to listen for His voice and to recognize it when He speaks. It has taken time to trust that His decisions are always right and in my best interest. Sometimes He whispers. Sometimes He just talks. Sometimes He shouts to get my attention. I know He wants to be part of my daily life. And I want to be part of His. We're FRIENDS. You can experience this same kind of relationship too. Prayer is simply talking with God and waiting for Him to talk back.

In order to enjoy deeper levels of conversation with a FRIEND, time spent together and intimacy are essential. This brings me to another way I "hear" Him talk with me. This involves the essential third box at the top of your Facing It Journal page – reading your Bible. Remember to think about your reading like a scavenger hunt. Be ready to experience fun, adventure, excitement, treasures, and FRIENDSHIP as you read one verse at a time or many. God speaks beautifully and profoundly through His written Word. Remember to ask, so you can receive word from Him. Remember to seek Him and His ways as you read, and He will be found. Remember to knock at His door, and He promises to open it and invite you in as FRIEND. More tips on how to read your Bible can be found in the Facing It Journal. For now, it's enough to know you need to be reading in your Bible daily.

Those are my every day essentials: the Lord's Prayer, personal prayers, and Bible reading. I hope they become yours as well. These disciplines are essential to my growing understanding of God and to my personal FRIENDSHIP with His Son. They are essentials to helping me FACE the challenges of life as a handicapper. They are essentials to helping anyone in any circumstance. Remember, He calls us FRIENDS if we obey His commands. How can we know His commands? We can know His commands by talking with Him in prayer and listening for His answers. And we can come to know Him better and better every time we pick up our Bible and learn what He requires of His followers. Like any FRIENDSHIP, the pleasure is in the knowing of another, and that takes time. Start marking off those three boxes at the top of your *Facing It Journal* page. (This is so important that if you're using your own journal; make a space to do the same thing.) Go for it!

We are now ready to move on to our fourth F of good CHOICES. The fourth F of our 4 good CHOICES concerns a FUTURE FACE TO FACE MEETING. Our roller coaster is slowing down to a clean, easy entrance to the exit gate. I'm glad. I'm ready to get off this ride! Are you? Here comes CHOICE #4

Chapter 9

The 4 Fs of Choice:

FUTURE FACE TO FACE MEETING

> FUTURE FACE TO FACE MEETING – Definition: "Now we see but a poor reflection as in a mirror; then we shall see face to face. Now I know in part; then I shall know fully, even as I am fully known." (1st Corinthians 13:12)

For me, this is the best part of the Good News that Jesus came to share with us. This life is not all there is. We are made for eternity. And one day, when we leave this physical world, we, who CHOOSE to name Jesus as our Lord and Forgiver, will see Him FACE TO FACE, in fullness of joy. The One Who laid down His earthly life for us, will be actively welcoming each of His followers to our Heavenly Home. The relationship that begins on Earth will continue forever in Heaven. Each person who CHOOSES to accept His offer of eternal life by CHOOSING Him will one day look into His FACE and know fully, what we now only know partly – all the WHYS of WHY we are now having to FACE IT, and more. I greatly anticipate this meeting. He is my best FRIEND, Lord and Forgiver, and I cannot wait to see what He really looks like, up close. I'm smiling even now, as I write. The perfect Son of God Who takes away the sins of all who CHOOSE to trust Him, will one day welcome me to His eternal kingdom, FACE TO FACE. Me – Pam Van Hook! And you, too, if you CHOOSE the A, B, C, D, and E of FAITH! Amazing! Thrilling! Exciting! Worlds beyond the most daring of roller coaster rides. This will be for me, pure pleasure, pure awe, pure worship of the King of Kings and Lord of Lords! I can't wait!

Knowing that this meeting will take place in my FUTURE, makes my now all right with me and puts any WHYS I have on hold. When I consciously make good CHOICE #4 and CHOOSE to think about my FUTURE FACE TO FACE MEETING in a place called Heaven, I am instantly lifted up and away. This CHOICE can help you too.

What follows is a long personal account. It's so long that I'm not going to put it in a box like my other personal accounts. (Just because it's long doesn't mean you can skip reading it. It's about the hardest IT we ever have to FACE.)

 ## Life and Death

Christian Michael Pastor was his name. He was born on April 23, 1994 and he died on April 26, 1994. Yes. He was 3 days old. There is a mirror of beveled glass and dark wood frame that graces the wall of his parents' bedroom. A mirror given to grieving parents by a grieving uncle and auntie. It is a mirror of remembrance. Remembrance of a brief, beautiful life lived here on earth. The truth of God's promise in 1st Corinthians 13:12 is written on the back of this mirror – "Now we see but a poor reflection as in a mirror; then we shall see face to face. Now I know in part; then I shall know fully, even as I am fully known." Christian Michael Pastor. One of our family. A baby held closely, whose breath I felt on my cheek. One dear to our family and friends. One dear to me. One dear to God. In the telling of his story, may he become dear to you.

It was April 2, 1994. There was a big party going on at our house. It was a baby shower for the baby to come and his mama, my brother's wife. (Aunt E. to our girls and a sister to me.) The house was all decorated, treats were on the table, and the place was buzzing with the voices of 30 women gathered to celebrate: close family, extended family, church family, and friends. The invitation sent out had read: "A Celebration of Life for Elizabeth Pastor and Baby Christian Michael!" I had given several baby showers before. This one was unique. Here's why.

Four months into her third pregnancy, Aunt E. had a routine blood test. The results suggested that there was a possibility of some sort of genetic problem. What? Nothing like this had ever happened before in our family. Must be a glitch in the testing. Both of their other children were perfectly beautiful, smart and adorable: Paul James was 8 years old and little Irene

242

Autry was 5 years old. The doctor tried to convince Aunt E. to have an amniocentesis done, but to what purpose? It would have put the baby she was carrying at some risk and we knew it wouldn't be pleasant for her. So, no thank you. Not yet.

As the months wore on, more problems with this pregnancy became evident. By now, we knew Aunt E. was carrying a baby boy. A baby boy! There were questions about the health of his kidneys and his heart, and it seemed that something genetic was not quite right. At the beginning of the seventh month, she and my brother were convinced to go ahead with an amniocentesis, because the doctors needed to know exactly what to expect at birth, so they would be ready for action if emergency measures were necessary for the baby. My brother received the results of the amniocentesis over the phone. The baby boy Aunt E. was carrying had a chromosome disorder, called Trisomy 13. The doctor told my brother that this particular genetic disorder was, "incompatible with life." The doctor suggested that surgically terminating this pregnancy would probably be the kindest course of action for Aunt E. and the family. This baby boy might die in the womb, might die during labor and delivery, and would certainly not live long, if he made it alive into the world. If he made it through labor and delivery, he almost certainly would be severely deformed and difficult to look at. Dark news.

For about three days despair and confusion reigned. These burdened parents prayed and prayed, and were prayed for. What should they do? What action, if any, should they take? Then, the Lord of Life, spoke to the hurting hearts of two of His followers, as they prayed for His help. He said, "You watch Me deliver. Wait on God." That was enough. The WHYS didn't matter now, because of Who had just spoken. The grace and peace of God was poured all over Aunt E. and my brother, over my nephew and my niece, and over all in our circle of family and friends who knew the Powerful One, Who had spoken with authority, clarity, comfort, assurance, and mercy. Aunt E. and my brother knew that Voice. They trusted that Voice. These parents declined the prescribed termination and decided to wait on God and watch Him deliver.

Incredibly, joy entered their lives and ours. Joy! Life was inside Elizabeth and we were going to enjoy this precious little one for as long as God allowed. Aunt E. knew her time with this baby boy would be limited. OK. No one knew how long this baby, who kicked and rolled and hiccuped in his mama's womb, would live. OK. Aunt E. counted every day she continued to carry him, as one in which she would get to know her son. OK. She determined that this would be her "bonding time" with the baby boy they had already named, Christian Michael. OK. Our family bonded with him too, during this womb-time. We laid hands all over Aunt E.'s big tummy and felt Christian Michael's presence in his kicks and turns and rollovers. He was one fun kid! We talked to him and sang to him. If he could hear, he knew the many different voices of his family. Even if he couldn't hear, he had to know how loved he was. After all, only inches separated us from him. And love knows no boundaries. How we all loved that curled up treasure Aunt E. was carrying.

His parents knew, and my family knew, and many others knew, Christian Michael Pastor was no accident. No mistake. No genetic mess-up by an uncaring God. His life was important. His life had great significance. His life was meaningful and purposeful. God formed him and loved him as much as any perfectly formed baby on the planet. We all were going to enjoy his life as much as possible. So we were having the party, the Celebration of Life for him and for his mama. All who attended, brought gifts and cards of love and encouragement for Aunt E. and the family. I know the biggest gift of all to her was the presence of so many who loved and cared for her, for her sweet baby, and for her family. Yes, there were tears of joy and of sadness. Laughter and mourning mixed as gifts were opened. But, isn't that life? Life. We were there to celebrate life, and we did. Because the Author of Life was at the center of it all. Jesus.

The day came for him to be delivered. It was a beautiful, warm, sunny, spring day in Oregon, with birds singing outside the delivery suite at the hospital. Yes. She carried him to term. He lived that long. She and he endured labor and delivery. He lived that long. The doctor handed newborn Christian Michael into my brother's hands. He was tiny and wrinkled and blue-gray. Not moving. Not crying. Not breathing. The doctor was in no hurry to try and help him do so, and that was OK. All had agreed ahead of time, that there would be no unnecessary medical intervention. Remember, Trisomy 13 is "incompatible with life." That's true. Everyone had tried to prepare for this death. All present at his delivery thought he was dead. That his life on earth was over, before it ever began.

244

Then, as nurses were comforting and assisting Aunt E., my brother began to massage Christian Michael's tiny chest and breathe over him, "Come on, son … come on, son …." The baby took a breath! And then another. And another. The doctor was amazed. The nurses were amazed. Aunt E. and my brother were amazed. He was breathing!

Family and friends were awaiting the birth news in the hospital hall, the waiting room, and at home by their phones. Instead of exiting the delivery room with news of death, my brother came out with the news that we could soon see our new baby. I think all of us felt a rush of urgency to see him, touch him, and tell him we loved him, this side of the womb. We didn't know how long he would be with us.

I remember distinctly thinking to myself, "I don't care what he looks like. He will be beautiful to me." (My husband and I had read up on Trisomy 13 and the devastating physical defects that were possible.) As Jim and I entered the room, Paul James was laughing, and so were Aunt E. and my brother. Laughter fell on our ears as we entered the room of a Trisomy 13 baby. What was going on? As any 8 year old would, Paul James had wanted to see his baby brother unwrapped. What did he look like naked? And as we were entering the room, Paul James' baby brother had just peed all over his hand. The plumbing was working! As Paul James got cleaned up, Jim and I leaned over our new nephew, as he was getting mopped up. What would he look like? He was beautiful. Fully formed on the outside. Genetically dysfunctional, but, oh so handsome. Thank You, God. What blessing! His eyes were tightly closed and his hands were closed in tiny fists, but he looked whole. He was God's gift.

Then Aunt E. did the unthinkable. She asked us if we wanted to hold him. Hold him? Oh, God. Yes! Please! My arms ached for him. But how could she give him up? How could she let go? How could my brother? How could Paul James? How could "big sister" Irene? How could they let him go to other arms? What honor and joy. How could his mama and closest family, be willing to give him up out of their arms, knowing that at any moment, he could stop breathing and die? I don't know if I could have let loose of him had he been my newborn baby. But with a loving smile on her face, Aunt E. asked my brother to please take him from her and lay him in my arms. My brother gently gave his son to his sister.

How can such heart wrenching love exist? To feel his form. Don't let anyone tell you that the human body isn't important. It is a sacred creation of God Himself, and worthy of awe and tenderness, no matter the appearance or number of chromosomes. How good it was to hold him close and feel his breath, stroke his hair, kiss his tiny wrinkled neck, and tweak his nose. (He had a very distinguished nose.) He smelled so sweet and babyish. It was obvious to all, that indeed, something quite devastating was wrong with this little body, but that evening, in the hospital suite, we had a pizza party. You heard right. A pizza party!

So many people came and visited. And Aunt E. invited all who came, to hold this special baby boy. All. The only life that Christian Michael would know, in this world, would be this room of family and friends, holding him, changing his diaper, feeding him, and loving him. The hospital staff was astounded at the crowd and the atmosphere in that room. There was a mix of celebration, joy, grief, peace, impending loss, and overwhelming love. God was with us in that room. His very angels graciously attended all who entered. It was a holy place, with a holy purpose. Life and death and Life would meet within the confines of those walls. It was apparent to all who entered.

Over the course of three days, 72 people came into that room and got to hold Christian Michael. Each had their photo taken with him as a remembrance for Aunt E. and the family. Many of these 72 came numerous times. That room was a hubbub of life. Children came with parents. Toys and food and drinks were all over the place. There were flowers and balloons and cards and presents in all corners of the room. Space was at a premium. Life was going on all around our new baby. Cousins, family, and friends enjoyed playing in a new place and entertained Irene. She was so young that she couldn't know the expected outcome of her new baby's arrival. But 8 year old Paul James knew. He knew. And he was whole heartedly and heart-breakingly attentive to his mom, his dad, his sister and his new baby brother. He was attentive to all visitors. He diligently and lovingly passed out Kleenex to those visiting, whose hearts would overflow to their eyes. He so loved his new brother and all who came with love into that room. (I need a Kleenex now.) He knew his time with his baby brother was going to be short, yet he graciously attended to the needs of others.

Soon, each visitor became acquainted with a distressing routine. Christian Michael never seemed to suffer pain, but he would cease to breathe. Often. When he would quit breathing, whoever was holding him would quickly get him into my brother's hands. Whoever was holding Christian Michael when he would experience this physical distress, could feel his heart race and pound and then stop. And race and pound and then stop. And then he would begin to turn blue. This happened so many times over the course of three days, that it almost seemed as if he could just continue forever with a heart that could race, and stop, and be jump started again. That he could just continue to go from pink, to blue, to gray, and then back to pink, forever.

But no. After an incredible three days of loving him, holding him, memorizing his face and form, he didn't go back to pink from gray. After three days of being close together with family and friends in the pretty hospital suite that had become home for him and us, our Christian Michael quit breathing for the last time. And was called home by a Voice I know he recognized. "Christian Michael Pastor, come out!"

A close family friend was holding him when the familiar episode occurred. He began to turn blue and she quickly handed him over to my brother. I truly expected the routine to continue: blue to gray and back to pink. But it didn't. The room fell silent as all eyes were on the baby and my brother. We could tell this wasn't the routine. My brother's shoulders began to shake with sobs and he said, "He's gone." He's gone. Gone. I looked to Aunt E., my mom, my husband, our family, our friends. Gone. Tears and sobs fill the room. Death had claimed one of ours. Darkness fell in the sunny, spring-lit room, with the unspeakable heaviness of death. Mourning. Grief. Separation. My brother said through tears falling on his baby's face, "Now I have just a taste of what it must have been like for God to give up His Son." Oh God. More tears. All in the room were trapped, staring at the unmovable stone of death.

Those who could, held his tiny, lifeless body one more time. Not all could bear to. I understood. I wanted to hold him once more. I'd never held one who'd just left his body behind, to answer the call of the Lord of all life. I felt pain. Grief. Darkness. Terrible separation. What an intimate sharing in the circle of mourners. And then, just like with Mary and Martha, Jesus showed up and moved the immoveable rock. The very One Who had called Lazarus out of his tomb, made His Presence known in that hospital room. The One Who had just called out Christian Michael's name and received him into His arms, brought comfort and peace and hope, to all who BELIEVED. The darkness of death was flooded with Light. Oh yes!

Jesus showed up. Yes, you heard right. Jesus showed up! As we prayed and mourned, He answered with mercy and grace and love and comfort — all is not lost. Once, for all, Jesus conquered death. Thank God. He gently reminded us, that we who BELIEVE will see Christian Michael again. FACE TO FACE. In Heaven. God's Word says so. God says so. And Jesus proved it when He walked out of His own grave by the power of the Living God.

Yes, there were still tears and grief. There probably always will be, as we remember our sweet Christian Michael. But we don't remain stuck in front of that awful cave. Jesus called out the name of Christian Michael Pastor, a Trisomy 13 baby here on earth, now complete in every way in Heaven. Some day, Jesus will call each of us out and away. By name. And He has all authority in Heaven and on earth, to do so. Praise God for His gift of eternal life! Some day, when my spirit leaves this body, not only will I see my Savior FACE TO FACE but also it will be my great joy to look into the crowd of loved ones who have gone on before, and see the very distinctive face of my nephew, Christian Michael Pastor. Heaven is a real place. Heaven is our real home. And oh, what a homecoming I am looking forward to! Get ready for a huge, Auntie hug, Christian Michael! I'm comin'! And the party will be fantastic!

Meaningful and Purposeful

Before we leave the story of Christian Michael, I'm thinking that there are some things I still want to make clear to you, and I'm thinking that both you handicappers and caregivers need to write down your thoughts, concerning my thoughts. Remember, that in the telling of his story I said that his brief life was meaningful and purposeful? I want to define these two words and then have us think about our own lives, as handicappers and caregivers. OK?

> Meaningful – Definition: Having meaning. Having a serious, important, or useful quality or purpose.

Even though from the get-go Christian Michael was forming up as a Trisomy 13 baby, his brief life was meaningful. Note the definition again. His life had a serious, important, and useful quality of purpose in the lives of his caregivers and those that loved him. He was born so genetically disabled, that we all knew he wouldn't live long in this world, if at all. But, oh, his life was meaningful! So much love was poured on him and his family. The dignity of his little body, was heartbreakingly beautiful. The doctor had told my brother that this baby's physical problems were "incompatible with life." He was right. And he was wrong. So much "life" surrounded this baby before and after his birth. I learned so much about life, from his life and his death. So did many others. Hundreds of people were impacted by his life and death at the time, and maybe thousands by now.

Every time I share his story, hearts are moved past grief and darkness, towards light and life and love. In women's ministry, I have mourned many times with mamas that have had to say goodbye to their little ones. My experience with Christian Michael has helped me to help them. I know the same is true for Aunt E., my brother, and all of our family. The Bible tells us that when we suffer, it is not for nothing, but that we may be able to comfort others, when they suffer what we already have experienced. Doesn't that make sense? Only those who have lost a baby close to them really know the fullness of the experience. Only someone who is blind can really know the blindness of another. Only someone cut down in the prime of youth with muscular dystrophy can relate completely with another in the same boat. Only someone FACING a physical disability can know what that means to another. Only the caregivers of a loved one FACING physical disability fully know what it's like to be a caregiver. Those not directly involved can empathize, but not truly "know." We can learn, grow, recover, and be inspired by those who really know what we are going through. As handicappers and caregivers, we are in meaningful positions. Our disabilities have meaning. We can help others.

God doesn't goof up. There is meaning and purpose to all He allows. Yes, He could have formed our baby nephew perfectly. Instead, we had the honor of loving and caring for a Trisomy 13 baby who lived just 3 days.

Were you born with your physical disability, or like me, did it strike you like a rattlesnake, later in life? Have you always been the caregiver to your capper, or like Jim, were you surprised with this responsibility? Would both of you, cappers and caregivers, please review the definition of *meaningful*, and apply the word to your life? Your life is meaningful. Does this make sense to you? What do you want to write?

Purposeful – Definition: Having or showing determination or resolve: having a useful purpose; intentional.

Long before my handicaps hit me, I learned first hand, the definition of purposeful. I watched Aunt E. and my brother determine to make the very best of what the world would call a tragedy. It was with purpose that God created Christian Michael and it was with purpose he came into our lives. God was determined to demonstrate His power, and love and comfort, through our little baby. (God knew full well, how meaningful our baby's life would be — 2,000 years ago God's baby had showed up in a manger, wrapped in swaddling clothes, with little hands and feet that one day would feel the bite of Roman nails. God's Baby, Jesus, would give meaning to every life ever conceived.)

Not only was God purposeful and intentional in His creation of Christian Michael. Not only were Aunt E. and my brother and family determined and resolved to allow God's purposes to unfold. But, our little Trisomy 13 baby was determined. Determined to live as well and as long as God allowed. I remember thinking to myself, as I held him in that room buzzing with life: "He is not giving up. His heart is racing and pumping so furiously that I can see it moving his little chest. He's no quitter. If ever, I am FACED with trouble of any kind, I am determined to remember this little one lying on my lap. I am determined to copy him, and never give up, until God calls me home to Heaven. He is so determined to live; no matter the number of chromosomes he's been dealt. He keeps trying. He keeps breathing, even though the effort furrows his tiny brow. The same needs to be true for me. Thank you, little one. Thank you. You are my inspiration." I remember thinking that. Little did I know how much I'd need his inspiration, in my own life: mentally, emotionally, spiritually, and physically. Thank you, Lord, for allowing Christian Michael Pastor to grace my life with his.

 # Concluding My Interlude —
April 23, 2004

Do you remember the Interlude after FRUSTRATION, and just before FURY? I wrote about the pretty, round, pink and orange tiled, mirror I *had* to have on our Ikea shopping trip. It was quite an important purchase and positively influenced my every day experience of FACING my handicaps, as well as my daily writing of FACING IT. Here is the rest of the mirror story. The part I left out until now.

As you recall, I *had* to have that mirror and my sweet husband purchased it for me. I was so excited as we drove home in the dark to Portland and our house on the hill. I was trying to figure out why in the world this mirror was so important to me, when all of a sudden I realized what the date was. Riding in the dark, close to Jim, I said, "Oh my goodness! It's April 23rd. It's Christian Michael's tenth birthday!" The last time we had purchased a mirror, it was the mirror of beveled glass and dark wood frame. The mirror of remembrance given to Aunt E. with a verse of hope written on the back: "Now we see but a poor reflection as in a mirror; then we shall see face to face. Now I know in part; then I shall know fully, even as I am fully known."

On what would have been Christian Michael's tenth birthday here on earth, I had been drawn to another mirror. A mirror that brightened my work place and helped me FACE my own disabilities and yours. A beautifully bright mirror. A mirror of sparkling inspiration that beckoned me to think and pray and write. I am convinced that God was having fun with me. It was no coincidence that I laid my one blue eye on what I now call my FACING IT mirror, on April 23, 2004. I am so grateful to be able to gaze into this mirror each day, and know that one day I will see my Lord and my nephew, FACE TO FACE! Isn't God gracious and awesome?

Two mirrors purchased in ten years: one of sweet remembrance and hope, and one of bright inspiration and hope. Both tied together in the same Scripture. God is so good.

Now, to you cappers and caregivers — how about you? Please review the definition of *purposeful* and write down what comes to mind concerning your own situations. Go!

DO – Readers

DO CHOOSE to look into your study Bible and find out what Heaven is like. DO make the CHOICE to receive Jesus as your Lord and Forgiver, because I want to see you there. I want to meet each and every one of you cappers and caregivers. Heaven is so wonderful that simple words cannot describe it fully. But, it is fun to dig into God's Word and look at our real home — the place God intended us to be all along. (But that sin thing got in our way.) I don't want to tell you too much about this wonderful FUTURE home and the One waiting to greet us, so DO look into it on your own. Please write down what you find out about Heaven in God's Word. Do you want to be there FACE TO FACE one day with the Lover of your soul? Do you want to meet me and Jim and Christian Michael, and any and all who are dear to you, who claim Jesus as Lord? DO look into the Bible and see what you can look forward to. Heaven is a real place. What are you thinking? Will you DO this DO?

 **DON'T – Readers**

DON'T fall for the lie that this life is all there is, and then you die. End of story. In fact, DON'T fall for any of the world's lies, Satan's lies, or even little white lies you might try to tell yourself, concerning life or no life after death. DON'T neglect to read your study Bible, because, "The Word of God is living and active. Sharper than any double-edged sword, it penetrates even to dividing soul and spirit, joints and marrow; it judges the thoughts and attitudes of the heart. Nothing in all creation is hidden from God's sight. Everything is uncovered and laid bare before the eyes of Him to Whom we must give account." (Hebrews 4:12-13.) DON'T try to skip past the reality that we are created by God as eternal beings and all of us will be met FACE TO FACE by "the One to Whom we must give account." Please DON'T assume, as many do, that you can skip the A, B, C, D, and E of FAITH in Jesus as Rescuer and Lord, and skip on into eternal life on your own. The Bible makes it very clear, that we are saved for eternal life with God by only One Name — Jesus. Please DON'T pass Him by. Please DON'T pass up His free gift of eternal life with God and an abundant life now, here on earth. Please DON'T.

Please DON'T put yourself in the awful place of one day meeting FACE TO FACE with the One and Only Son of God, Whom you have rejected. That will not be a time of joy, worship and reunion. That will be a time of awful reality. A time to know what you have lost by your rejection of God's love to us through His Son's death and resurrection. A time when you will bow your knee, whether you want to or not, and confess that Jesus is indeed Lord, whether you want to or not. The Bible says that even though Jesus is in His very nature, God, He humbled Himself and became a man. He humbled Himself even to death on a terrible Roman cross, in obedience to God — for us! And, "therefore God exalted him to the highest place and gave him the name that is above every name, that at the name of Jesus every knee should bow, in heaven and on earth and under the earth and every tongue confess that Jesus Christ is Lord, to the glory of God the Father." (Philippians 2:9-11) The Bible makes it crystal clear that every person who has ever lived will one day bow down and confess — either in awe and joy, or in awe and terror. Everyone. If you DON'T CHOOSE the A, B, C, D, and E steps to FAITH in Jesus as Forgiver and Lord, the awful truth is you will end up separated from God, forever. Forever. … This is as awful as awful can get. Forever separated from the God Who loves you so much that He suffered the cross to get you back to Himself. No life, no love, no light, no laughter, no hope, no peace, no communion with God, forever. Forever. The Bible calls this "the second death." Please DON'T CHOOSE to reject the lover of your soul — Yeshuah Messiah, Jesus, the Way, the Truth and the Life, and the only way to the Father. Please DON'T.

> One of my most favorite books to read and reread and reread again, in the whole wide world, is written by Randy Alcorn. The title is Deadline. I suggest you read it (or have someone read it to you, if you can't see well enough to read it yourself.) Randy creates a novel of memorable characters, an intriguing mystery, and descriptions of both Heaven and Hell that let you know for sure which way you want to be heading, when your soul exits your present residence. I wouldn't want to ruin the story for you by telling you which of the characters ends up in Heaven and which ends up in Hell, but Randy makes it abundantly clear, that no one will be happy with the Hell-CHOICE. The Hell-CHOICE, is hell.
>
> For those of you who prefer non-fiction, Randy Alcorn has also written an excellent treatise on heaven. It is wonderfully detailed, based on the Bible, and it is aptly titled, Heaven.

DON'T make the mistake of thinking Hell is going to be some big time get-together of fun-seeking, rough-edged, independent, free-thinkers. There is no get-together in Hell. Hell is eternal separation from God and all that is in and with Him. There is nothing but personal isolation, torment, darkness, and burning regret, forever. Forever and ever. Jesus spoke often of Hell, because He wanted His listeners to realize that it is, indeed, a real place. Jesus came to make clear our path to Heaven. Please CHOOSE His Way and DON'T let yourself slide, slip, trip, or proudly stride your way into Hell. The CHOICE is yours, now, here on earth. When you die, you *will* come FACE TO FACE with the Lord Jesus, Who holds the keys to both places: Heaven and Hell. I know He wants you with Him. I know I want you with Him. DON'T make the mistake that will cost you all eternity. Please DON'T.

How do you feel about this DON'T?

 DARE – Readers

This DARE, is almost too important to be called a DARE. This DARE requires a CHOICE from every person that has ever lived. So, that includes us cappers and caregivers. The CHOICE we make here on earth, decides how our FUTURE FACE TO FACE will go. DARE to give up self-centeredness and CHOOSE the Lover of your soul. DARE to CHOOSE life with God forever, starting now. DARE to believe and trust and be loyal to the Son of the Living God, Jesus. DARE to place your FAITH in Jesus.

DARE to put your WHYS on hold and really live in the here and now, looking forward to a FUTURE FACE TO FACE MEETING with your Forgiver and Lord. DARE to begin to know Him now, so when you look into His eyes and see His FACE, you won't be surprised. It will be a true homecoming and His warm welcome will be better than anything you can imagine. DARE to embrace Jesus of Nazareth, Yeshuah Messiah, Who is waiting to embrace you. Please DARE.

And I'll see you in Heaven, FACE TO FACE, if not here on earth. Together, we can explore the wonders God has prepared for those who CHOOSE His Son. Please DARE to come to Jesus now, because I want to hang out with

Him and with you, forever. DARE to become a follower of Jesus of Nazareth. Will you? CHOOSE Dear One, CHOOSE. CHOOSE to think of your future FACE TO FACE MEETING with Him in Heaven, every FACING IT day of your life. This is your next-to-last chance to write in this book. Will you take up this DARE? Write, Dear Ones, write!

Caregivers and Handicappers

Will you please reflect, think, pray, and ADAPT concerning Heaven? What do you want to write?

You are now ready to daily record your thoughts about a FUTURE FACE TO FACE MEETING with Jesus. You can use your journal to help you daily think about and anticipate all the joys awaiting those who BELIEVE. It helps me so much to daily place my thoughts on my FUTURE FACE TO FACE — to constantly direct my heart and mind toward Heaven. I know it will help you too.

Plan it. Do it. Record it.

CONCLUSION.

Well, if you've made it this far, you have FACED IT! You've FACED the 5 Fs of Reaction and the Big D roller coaster, and the 4 Fs of CHOICE. Congratulations! I am so pleased with you and your efforts. You have become writers and journalers. I'm glad for me, too. In the process of talking this book to you, I think I've also become a writer. I am actually beginning to enjoy my interactions with this keyboard and you. That's a surprise.

Now, at the end of our time together in this book, I urge you and I urge myself, to keep on journaling. I am certain the process of daily journaling will help us as handicappers and caregivers, to continue to FACE IT WELL. Here's to FACING IT, Dear Ones. How I love you all and long to see each one of you, FACE TO FACE, one day.

I want to close with some words that Jesus gave me one morning, near the end of the writing of this book. They came to me so fast, my pencil nearly burned a hole in the scrap paper I scribbled on. (It was 4:45 in the morning.) Here they are neatly typed.

Face to Face

Ancient Scriptures from of old, tell of shiny streets of gold
Where broken vessels are made whole,
When we reach our final goal.
Facing life now filled with love, as we wait to fly above,
Jesus is our all in all, when our name we hear Him call.

Broken vessels filled with light, as we daily fight the fight,
In the power of His might, in the Spirit, what a sight!

FACE TO FACE with Him Who knows
My name, my frame, and all my woes.
FACE TO FACE I'll fully know,
As I am fully known.

In the power of His grace, what He allows, I will embrace,
Until one day I see Him, FACE TO FACE.

No more failures, furies, fears, no more frustration into tears,
All my final hurdles past, in my Savior's arms at last.

Oh, to hear my Savior's voice, with joy approve my CHOICE.
To see my Lord and Friend, as to my knees I bend
and look into His eyes, FACE TO FACE.

To FACE God's Son and hear, "Well done My servant dear."
To know Him close and near, what blessing bright!
As I gaze into the mirror that is at last so crystal clear,
I will finally walk with Him into His Light.

This feels like a prayer to me. So I will end with Amen. Amen.

About the Author

Pam Van Hook is a God-gifted communicator and teacher. *Facing It* is her first book, and is drawn from her personal experience. In 1999 Pam, a wife, mother of three and grandmother of two, was leading a healthy, vibrant life when she was suddenly stricken with a variety of severe and unexplainable medical conditions. Pam is now physically handicapped having lost the use of her right eye and can no longer walk without the use of a walker. While now more than 8 years later Pam's medical condition has not improved, God's faithfulness and His work in her life has brought her peace and served as a testimony to thousands.

A leader and Bible study teacher for more than 16 years at Beaverton Christian Church, Pam's passion is speaking to groups of 10 to 1,000, about her faith and about the practical help contained in *Facing It* and the companion volume, *The Facing It Journal*. Pam has a Bachelor's Degree in Speech from Cal State Fullerton, practical training as a "Precepts" teacher, and many years experience as mentor and teacher. She brings a lively, humorous, informative, interactive, and uplifting message to all audiences, but especially to those having to FACE IT.

Pam and her husband, Jim, live in Beaverton, Oregon. With the publication of this book, Pam has entered a new phase of life, reaching a wider audience through Pam Van Hook Ministry, and as a nationwide speaker. Her emphasis is on applying the principles in *Facing It* to all of life's challenges.

Pam is available to speak at:

Churches
Conferences
Retreats
Seminars

Contact information:
www.facingit.org
pam@facingit.org

CPSIA information can be obtained
at www.ICGtesting.com
Printed in the USA
FSHW022116070719
59776FS